Vigilance and Habituation

A Neuropsychological Approach

Jane F. Mackworth

Penguin Books

To N.H.M.
The Inspiration of this book

Penguin Books Ltd, Harmondsworth,
Middlesex, England
Penguin Books Inc., 7110 Ambassador Road,
Baltimore, Md 21207, U.S.A.
Penguin Books Australia Ltd, Ringwood,
Victoria, Australia

First published 1969
Copyright © Jane F. Mackworth, 1969

Made and printed in Great Britain by
C. Nicholls & Company Ltd
Set in Monotype Times

Penguin Education

Penguin Science of Behaviour
General Editor: B. M. Foss

Physiological Psychology
Editor: K. H. Pribram

Vigilance and Habituation
A Neuropsychological Approach
Jane F. Mackworth

WITHDRAWN

Penguin Science of Behaviour

This book is one in an ambitious project, the *Penguin Science of Behaviour*, which covers a very wide range of psychological inquiry. Many of the short 'unit' texts are on central teaching topics, while others deal with present theoretical and empirical work which the Editors consider to be important new contributions to psychology. We have kept in mind both the teaching divisions of psychology and also the needs of psychologists at work. For readers working with children, for example, some of the units in the field of Developmental Psychology will deal with psychological techniques in testing children, other units will deal with work on cognitive growth. For academic psychologists, there will be units in well-established areas such as Learning and Perception, but also units which do not fall neatly under any one heading, or which are thought of as 'applied', but which nevertheless are highly relevant to psychology as a whole.

The project is published in short units for two main reasons. Firstly, a large range of short texts at inexpensive prices gives the teacher a flexibility in planning his course and recommending texts for it. Secondly, the pace at which important new work is published requires the project to be adaptable. Our plan allows a unit to be revised or a fresh unit to be added with maximum speed and minimal cost to the reader.

Above all, for students, the different viewpoints of many authors, sometimes overlapping, sometimes in contradiction, and the range of topics Editors have selected will reveal the complexity and diversity which exist beyond the necessarily conventional headings of an introductory course.

B.M.F.

Contents

Editorial Foreword

Every researchable field of human endeavour progresses through a series of stages: first, discovery with its enthusiastic breakthroughs into knowledge heretofore hidden or grasped only implicitly; second, the accumulation of detail which fogs the initially clear view of the matter in hand; third, a turning point which promises deeper understanding and explorations in directions unexpected in the initial inquiry. Finally, the issues become fully drawn, a synthesis becomes possible, the harvest is in, to be enjoyed in preparation for the next leap in discovery.

This volume on vigilance is written during the third of these stages. Thus, the book reviews the detail which has accumulated since Norman Mackworth's pioneering work on vigilance and heralds the turning point that unexpectedly brings into play a host of studies which deal with the mechanism of decrementing psychological processes. New vistas thus come into view: the role of the nervous system in constructing a model of its input; the analysis of orienting into sampling and registrational components; the organization of expectancy and therefore of arousal and activation; the relationship between all of this and signal detection theory.

The turning is a fascinating albeit difficult stage to represent in a book. No polished synthesis can be given, yet hundreds of studies must be taken into account and accounted for. Jane Mackworth does a remarkable job of this. One suspects that no one other than a Mackworth, immersed in vigilance research from its inception, could have done the job at all. The surprise is that immersion has not drowned vision, that new directions are signalled to the scientific community and that their importance to the general weal is made clear. This requires vigilance, the activity of so observing that novelties can be detected within a background of reactions habituated through familiarity. Thank you, Jane Mackworth, for your vigilance on vigilance.   K.H.P.

Introduction

The main purpose of this book is to emphasize the growing links between psychology and neurophysiology. In particular, it is proposed that the *performance decrement* found in the course of a wide variety of somewhat monotonous decision-making tasks is related to the physiological phenomenon of *habituation*. Active inhibition of neural responses to a repetitive series of stimuli can make overt muscular responses less likely, or reduced in speed or accuracy. This active inhibition is related to the formation of a neural model of the stimulus. The mental model or engram incorporates not only the physical characteristics of a repetitive series of stimuli, but also the temporal pattern. The *vigilance task* usually presents many 'unwanted' background or non-signal events for each wanted signal. The main idea underlying this book is that the decrement in detections or reduced speed of response to these rare signals is related to habituation of the specific and non-specific neural responses to the many unwanted background events, from which the signal must be discriminated. The nature of the decrement in performance may depend on the relative importance of the two kinds of neural response, the evoked potential and the arousal response, as well as on the expectancy of the subject as to the probability that a forthcoming event will be a signal. Decrements in performance are also found in more active tasks, such as tracking, which require a positive response to every event. Here, too, it is proposed that habituation of the neural responses to these repetitive events is a factor in the decrement.

The age-old gap between mind and matter is quickly being narrowed by the disciplines of psychophysiology and neuro-psychology. The psychophysiologist is showing that neural responses are affected by the plans, programmes and interests of the subject; the neuropsychologist is finding that the concept of attention (once scorned as being too vague) can be embodied in physiological changes. The properties of the stimulus that capture the interest or lead to a failure in performance due to lack of alert attention can now be measured in both psychological and physiological terms. Vigilance has, therefore, become a three-dimensional living body of research linking physiology, psychology and the realities of everyday life. Anyone with a scientific interest in attention and its physiological basis may gain further understanding of the complex interrelations from these pages.

It is necessary for the psychologist to be familiar with the outlines of neurophysiology, and for the brain researcher to have a knowledge of the relevant psychological studies. It is hoped that this book will act as a guide for these two groups, and will help to point out the many gaps in knowledge that require to be investigated. In particular, the relationship between certain personality traits and performance would seem a promising line of study. In addition, more detailed research into the relation between neurological changes and performance is needed before the hypothesis put forward in this book can be verified or discarded.

The author is most grateful for the support of the Radcliffe Institute, of Cambridge, Massachusetts, to whom this book owes its existence.

The remainder of the vigilance data is dealt with in *Vigilance and Attention: A Signal Detection Approach* (1970).

1 The Nature of the Vigilance Task

One of the guiding factors in the evolution of animals has been the principle that change is dangerous. The organism is bombarded with a continuous stream of stimuli, and by neglecting those which are predictable and readily recognizable as unimportant, all the mechanisms of detection and response are left free to react at maximum efficiency to the new and potentially dangerous event. As we become used to them, stimuli disappear from our consciousness. The ticking clock is no longer noticed, even the roaring subway train outside the window becomes a shadowy background in life.

The brain is like a great country, in which the final decisions for allocation of resources and manpower are made by one man. He can only do his job by being relieved of all the minor decisions. A hierarchy of decision makers filters out data until only that material which is judged to be of vital importance is handed to him. This system is necessary to avoid over-loading the head of the hierarchy; it is designed to maintain the status quo; only those events which seriously threaten the stability of the country will be passed on for final decision, unless the leader has indicated that he wishes to consider events relating to a particular subject. Such a situation does have certain disadvantages. It may be difficult for the head to make clear to his subordinates just what kind of events he believes to be important, and he may never see the somewhat unusual event that seems to his subordinates to be too small for his attention, yet it might contain the very facts suggesting new and dangerous changes that urgently need the attention of the highly skilled superior decision-maker.

The same difficulty is seen in a vigilance task. Here there is a stream of events which have to be neglected. Occasionally there is a small change in one of these events, and this small change is the signal which has to be detected. During the Second World War it was noticed that enemy submarines were appearing in waters which had been recently searched by observers of Coastal Command. Sir Frederic Bartlett of the Cambridge Psychological Laboratory was asked to make a study of the effects of fatigue on the radar detection of such targets. This detection required a discrimination between the submarine target and other ships, such as fishing boats, which were much more frequent. The problem was taken up by Norman Mackworth (1950), who designed the clock test (see p. 17). To this and other tasks designed to investigate the same psychological phenomenon he gave the name of vigilance tasks, taking the term from the definition by Head (1926); 'When vigilance is high, mind and body are poised in readiness to respond to any event external or internal.' This can be compared with the definition of the 'degree of excitation' by Duffy (1934) as 'the extent to which the whole organism is activated or aroused' (see Duffy, 1962, p. 3). Mackworth (1950; 1961 edn., p. 252) suggested that the observed loss of accuracy was due to a state of inhibition produced by the regular repetition of the jumps of the clock hand. Sharpless and Jasper (1956) suggested that the vigilance decrement might be due to habituation of the neural response to the repetitive stimuli.

Habituation has been defined as a decrease in an innate response as a result of repetition of the stimulus (Hernández-Peón, 1960). Such innate responses include neural changes. Two kinds of neural response are considered in this book, the evoked potential and the arousal response or alpha block. Habituation of the arousal response may be mediated by the frontal cortex, which actively inhibits physiological responses to repeated events (Pribram, 1967; see p. 102).

A stimulus captures attention when it is new, unexpected or difficult to interpret. These factors produce the arousal response (see chapter 4). As these properties disappear with repetition, the response habituates. A stimulus that is repeated many times produces a gradually decreasing response.

Habituation is a phenomenon so widespread in the animal kingdom that it can be regarded as a basic property of animal life. In the higher animals one of its main functions is that described earlier. The neural response to repetitive events is reduced, so that these events no longer concern the decision-making level, which is thus left free to consider novel and potentially dangerous events. Habituation takes place more rapidly when overt response to the repetitive event is not required, and the study of habituation has largely concentrated upon this condition. Studies of learning, conditioning and signal detection have concentrated on the opposite end of the spectrum, where there is a high probability that an overt response will be required. The field of vigilance experiments investigates the intervening area. The majority of the events of the task require no overt response, but a small minority of events, the signals, do. Failure of attention to the important event results in either a failure to detect the small differences that make it a wanted signal, or a slower response to that signal. The task is such that for maximal performance, attention must be paid either continuously or at least to each of the repetitive events, most of which are unwanted, in the sense that no overt response is required. A decision must be made about each event: 'Is it a signal or not?' Such acts of attention have been termed observing responses (see Jerison, 1967a; also Mackworth, 1970).

Vigilance tasks therefore offer an opportunity to investigate the two interlocking processes, *habituation* of the effect of a repetitive event, and *learning* about the properties and probabilities of a signal event requiring response. Despite the growing number of experiments, the area is only tentatively outlined by fact, and one of the aims of this book is to indicate the gaps and contradictions, in the hope that more systematic studies of the interactions between several variables may increase our understanding of the workings of the decision process at its simplest level. The fairly recent application of *signal detection* theory to vigilance, with the concept of the distinction between criterion and sensitivity, should resolve some of the contradictions. On the other hand, the concepts of vigilance theory may bring signal detection theory closer to real life. In life, the majority of events are ignored, and the important signal is often unexpected, its nature and source unknown, so that response may be far from the most efficient possible.

The term *decrement* is used throughout this book to mean a reduction in efficiency of performance between the beginning and end of a session.

In a vigilance task, the decrement may involve a reduction in the probability that a signal will be detected, or in the speed of response, or a change in both these measures. While the decrement has been studied most carefully in vigilance tasks, changes in performance may also be found in the course of other monotonous and repetitive tasks, even when a decision between various possible overt responses is required for every event. Such changes in performances may involve decreases in speed or accuracy or performance. The circumstances that influence the changes of performance during a monotonous task are by no means completely known. The requirements for continuous attention seem to be important, and less decrement occurs when the event rate is slower, so that fewer observing responses are required in unit time.

Neural Habituation.

The basic thesis of the book is that the decrement in monotonous tasks may be related to *two neural changes*. As a result of repetition of a stimulus, or of a series of stimuli, both the specific *evoked potential* and the less specific *arousal response* produced by the stimuli become habituated. That is, these neural responses are altered, reduced, or disappear, particularly in the cortex and reticular activating system. As a result of the reduction of the arousal response the internal 'noise' variability may be increased, while as a result of the reduction of the evoked potential both the repetitive event and the alteration in this event that constitutes a signal become less distinguishable from the noise. Thus both neural changes result in the distributions of the internal noise and the evoked potentials coming closer to each other, but the effect of these changes on performance depends on a number of factors that will be discussed.

The probable relationship between *arousal changes* and the vigilance decrement has been reviewed by a number of authors. Sharpless and Jasper (1956) were the first to suggest definitely that habituation of the arousal response might be causal in the vigilance decrement. Fiske and Maddi (1961), Frankmann and Adams (1962), Micko (1966), W. E. Scott (1966) and T. H. Scott (1957) have all discussed the decrement in terms of changes in arousal. It has, however, only recently been shown that there are *changes in the evoked potential* in a vigilance task, and these changes may be more important than changes in the background neural 'noise': in most vigilance tasks in which there is no difficulty in distinguishing the discrete repetitive event from the noise. It is also possible that habituation of the evoked potential may carry over from one session to the next. This habituation may result in increased sensitivity for the small change that constitutes a signal (Weber's law) which has been found in later sessions of certain tasks (Binford and Loeb, 1966; Broadbent and Gregory, 1965; Mackworth, 1970).

The *vigilance task* was designed by N. H. Mackworth (1950) to present a signal which in itself was fairly easy to detect, but the temporal probability of the signal was so low and so variable that it could not be learned. In the basic task all changes in stimulation external to the task are reduced to a minimum. No feedback is given. The signal itself has to be selected from an unchanging, randomly changing or repetitively changing background. Broadbent (1958) emphasized that the crucial factor in the occurrence of a decrement may be the requirement that more or less continuous attention must be paid to the display for maximum performance. If the subject is allowed to set his own pace, he may compensate for temporary blocks in attention by brief pauses in performance. This still leaves unanswered the question as to what causes an increase in the temporary blocks as time on task continues. No final answer to this question can be obtained as yet, but it is possible to point out the resemblances between vigilance tasks and other areas of psychophysiology to indicate that the decrement is perhaps a manifestation of an important evolutionary phenomenon rather than an inefficiency in an unusual kind of activity.

The term 'vigilance' was used by Head (1926) to describe a state of the central nervous system which could vary in level. The advent of various measures such as the electroencephalographic (E E G) records of brain activity have given us a great deal of information on this state, which has been discussed under the names of activation or arousal. Thus the name given by N. H. Mackworth (1950) implies that what is being measured in a vigilance task is a change in the level of arousal. Curiously enough, very little direct evidence on the changes in background level of activity of the central nervous system during a vigilance task has yet been published – more than twenty years after the first vigilance experiments – nor does it seem to be generally accepted that the decrement is directly related to a change in level of arousal. Since arousal level is dependent upon both external and internal changes, the situation is very complicated. The arousing properties of a stimulus depend on the past history of the subject, both before and during the actual test, and his own inner sources of arousal may be dependent not only on his personal history, but also on his genetic constitution (Duffy, 1962).

N. H. Mackworth (1957) enlarged Head's definition of vigilance by calling it a 'state of readiness to detect and respond to certain specified small changes occuring at random time intervals in the environment.' The definition contains an ambiguity, since a subject who is more 'ready' to detect a signal may also be more 'ready' to think he has detected one when in fact no signal has occurred. Thus a change in readiness may imply either a change in criterion or a change in sensitivity or both. Since there is evidence that both these changes may occur in vigilance tasks, the ambiguity in the definition does not destroy its relevance.

The experiments by N. H. Mackworth (1950) were carried out during the Second World War in order to see whether the monotony and unpredictability of a monitoring task could have a detrimental effect on performance, and if so how this effect could be prevented. While the problem arose from an immediate practical question, there had been previous relevant studies. Ditchburn (1943) decided that a subject's reaction time to a visual stimulus presented at unknown intervals increased as the intervals increased. Anderson *et al.* (1944) found an increased number of missed signals in a radar-like device in the second hour of watch-keeping as compared with the first. This decrement did not become significant until the third day of testing. Very high rates of signal presentation, up to 93 in 20 minutes, were employed (quoted by Mackworth, 1950).

The First Vigilance Tasks

N. H. Mackworth (1950) employed four kinds of task, two visual and two auditory. The first visual task was the clock test. In this a hand jumped 1/100 of the distance around an unmarked clock face every second. The signal was a double-length jump. Such signals occurred twelve times every half hour. The intervals between signals were 3/4, 3/4, 1½, 2, 2, 1, 5, 1, 1, 2, 3 and 10 minutes, in that order. This schedule was repeated every half hour, to complete the 2-hour session. A signal was regarded as detected if a response was given within 8 seconds. Five signals were given, with knowledge of results, in five minutes' practice at the beginning of each session.

The results showed that 15 per cent of signals were missed in the first half-hour and about 27 per cent in the other three half-hours. No significant changes occurred after the first half-hour. Subjects who were tested for a second time missed 6–10 per cent more signals throughout in the second run than in the first, but the decrement during the run was much the same with all groups. When the length of the clock hand was reduced to half, so that all movements were halved, this did not affect detection.

This experiment outlined the main problem being studied in vigilance tests. Why does this decrement in detection occur during the run? It is important to distinguish between the initial or maximal level of detection and the size of the decrement during the run. No firm relationship between these two aspects of the data has been established. As already mentioned, the term decrement in this book is reserved for a reduction in efficiency occurring during a run. This decrement may be measured between the first and last periods of the watch, or between alerted performance and the final period of the watch.

Other factors examined by Mackworth with the clock test were as follows:

1. *When rest pauses* of half an hour were given between half hour runs, no difference between the first and second half hour run was found.

2. *A telephone message* was sent to the subject during the second ten-minute interval ending the first hour of a continuous two-hour run. These subjects were expecting the telephone message throughout. It exhorted them to do even better in the second part of the test. As a result their performance was higher in the third half-hour than in the first. Performance in the first half hour was significantly worse than the control group, while their performance in the third half hour was as good as the initial level of the control group. Thus the *distracting* effect of listening for a message was actually harmful when the subjects were fresh. Once the message had been received performance showed the same decrement during the final hour as the control group showed in the initial hour. The alerting effect of the message only lasted for a brief period.

3. *Incentive.* An attempt was made to separate the alerting effect of the telephone from its incentive effect. The subjects were told that when a continuously moving arrow on an auxiliary display reached a red area they should be particularly alert for signals; this occurred during the third half-hour, but had no effect on performance.

4. *Knowledge of results* (KR). Subjects were informed by loudspeaker on each occasion whether they had missed a signal, correctly reported one, or incorrectly reported a signal that had not occurred. Subjects did the test on two occasions, one with and one without KR, (NKR) in counterbalanced order. The results were as follows:

When KR was given before the control run (NKR) there was no difference in over-all scores. When NKR was given first, there was a considerable improvement in the second KR run. These results may be interpreted on the assumption that the effects of KR carry over to later runs without KR. Further work on this problem will be discussed later. A comparison between the KR runs and the original clock-test group showed a significant difference between the later parts of the run, while there was no difference between the initial half hour. Thus there was evidence that KR reduced the decrement during the run. Further work on this problem will be discussed later. In general it supports the findings that KR reduces the decrement and improves performance on a later run.

5. *'Benzedrine'*. 10 mg of dl-amphetamine sulphate or a placebo were administered one hour before the test. In the control condition no tablets were given. All subjects received all conditions in a balanced design. No difference was found between the placebo and the control condition. There was no significant difference between the groups in the first half hour, but there were large differences in the later periods, since no significant decrement was found with benzedrine, while the control group showed the usual decrement. There was no evidence of any effect of benzedrine on later control runs. Benzedrine was also found to decrease the latency of response (see chapter 8).

6. *Signal interval.* An analysis was made of the probability of detection of each successive signal. Performance reached a maximum with the fifth signal, occurring five minutes after the beginning of the test, and then declined sharply. In the

second and remaining half-hours the lowest probability of detection was found after the first 3/4 minute interval. In these three later periods the best detection was found with the signals following the long intervals of five and ten minutes. Detection of signals following the intervals of less than one minute was significantly worse than detection of signals following the two longer intervals. Thus it was clear that the subjects displayed a definite expectancy about the temporal probability. Their expectancy was lowest immediately after a signal, and rose to a maximum after the longer intervals.

7. *Heat*. Subjects were acclimatized to heat by exposing them for two hours a day to effective temperatures (E T) of 97°F. Each subject monitored the clock test for two hours at normal atmospheric temperatures, and then on the following day monitored the test again at one of four temperatures. It was found that fewer signals were missed at the optimum E T of 79°F. At E T of 70°, 87·5° and 97°F more signals were missed. The decrement during the run showed a different picture. The increase in number of missed signals from the first to the second hour was minimal for the lowest E T and maximal for the highest. Moreover, it was found that experienced look-out men showed a smaller decrement at the high E Ts than did inexperienced men. The lowest E T of 70° was found to be cold by these acclimatized men. It is therefore possible that the cold provided a distracting effect for the men who were dressed only in shorts, but this slight extra stimulus might also help to maintain arousal.

There was a definite increase in reaction time with the increase in E T. The median reaction time (counting missed signals as high reaction times) was minimal for the E T of 79° and maximal for the E T of 97°.

The Radar Test

The second visual task was a synthetic radar test. This presented a mottled dark-green circular screen with a rotating beam of light. The subject was told to ignore the beam but to watch for a spot of light which lasted for 4 seconds. This spot could appear anywhere on the screen. The twenty-four signals per hour had the same schedule as in the clock test. Two levels of brightness of the spot were tested.

The results were similar to those with the clock test. The dim echo was more difficult and the bright echo was easier than the clock test. The dim echo showed a decrement of about 10 per cent decrease in detected signals. The detection of the bright echo fell by 10 per cent from the first to the third half hour but then improved slightly, so that the over-all decrement from the first to last period was only about 5 per cent.

Signal interval. The results here were quite different from the clock test. Minimum detection was found for the signals following the long intervals. It was felt that this might have been due to the fact that the signals appeared in more or less clock-wise order around the dial, in the sense that successive groups of signals appeared in successive areas. This may have been one reason why detection improved in the final half-hour.

Auditory Test

The first test presented a regular series of 'pings', with a faint echo occurring occasionally between two pings. These echoes could vary in pitch, and the subject had to write down how the pitch of the echo compared with the standard ping. It did not prove possible to score the written records. The percentage of missed signals showed an *improvement* during the first run, but in the second run the usual decrement was found. It was clear that during the first run learning obscured the decrement. The problem of learning during auditory tasks has often been encountered.

The second test presented a regular series of tones. The signal was a slightly longer tone. The tones occurred once every 18 seconds and lasted for 2 seconds. The signal lasted for 2·25 seconds.

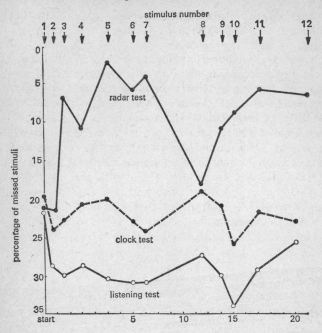

Figure 1 Stimulus-by-stimulus trends in clock, radar and listening tests (from N. H. Mackworth, 1950 ; 1961 edn, p. 17)

The decrement in this task was definitely larger than that found in the clock test. The first three points traced parallel lines for the two tests, but in the fourth half-hour there was a marked fall in the listening test. This fall occurred in both runs. Thus the total decrement from first to last was 16 per cent for the listening test while it was 10 per cent for the clock test. In the first run of the listening test there was a drop of over 21 per cent, while the second run showed a decrement of only 12 per cent.

1. *Signal Interval.* The relation of missed signals to the length of the previous interval since the last signal was almost identical for the listening test and the clock test (see Figure 1). This

emphasized the probability that the difference found with the radar test was related to some spatial factor.

2. *Knowledge of results*. The main effect of K R was dramatic. Instead of a decrement, there was a small improvement between the first and last half hours of the run. Once again, it was found that the effect of K R within a group depended on the order of presentation. Those subjects who received no knowledge of results in the first run showed a very large improvement in the second run with K R. The other group showed only a slight fall in going from the initial K R condition to the second N K R condition. The second run with N K R was better than any other group with this condition, even though the run was much worse than the K R run for the other group. This suggests, as before, that there was some learning in the K R run that improved performance on the later N K R run.

Other types of vigilance task

A brief outline of the various types of vigilance task is presented elsewhere (Mackworth, 1970). N. H. Mackworth found that there were more slow responses in later periods of the clock test, and many workers have shown that with an easily discriminable signal there is a significant decrease in speed of response as the session continues. A third type of vigilance task combines the two measures of signal detection and response time by presenting a series of signals, increasing in intensity until one is detected. This is known as the *effective threshold task* (see Bakan, 1955).

Theoretical Interpretations

There have been several theoretical interpretations of the vigilance decrement. Mackworth (1950) suggested that the decrement was due to *inhibition*. He discussed this inhibition in terms of experimental extinction, and pointed out that internal inhibition was facilitated by the highly repetitive and monotonous nature of the background events of the task. The clock hand went round and round, 'its time-rhythm un-changing, its steps always the same length except for the occasional double-length signal.' This book examines further the suggestion that the decrement is related to the repetitive non-signal events. Habituation is a decrement in response resulting from a repetition of the stimulus; Pribram (1967) and Sokolov (1963) have discussed the evidence in favour of the hypothesis that habituation of responses mediated by the cortex is due to inhibition (see chapter 5).

Mackworth also suggested that minute-by-minute changes in the *expectancy* of the subject as to the probability of a signal could account for fluctuations in the level of per-formance, and also for the fact that the decrement in per-formance was not complete, as might be expected from simple experimental extinction. The expectancy theory received additional support from the finding that a smaller percentage of signals were detected when the ratio of signals to non-signal events was smaller. The theory, as elaborated by C. H. Baker (1963a) and Deese (1955), was that the probability of detection of a signal depended on the ability of the subject to predict its occurrence.

Broadbent and Gregory (1963b, 1965) discussed the changes in terms of signal detection theory. They suggested that the decrement in performance was due to a change in *criterion*, the subject becoming less willing to make a positive response as the watch proceeded. (See also Jerison and Pickett, 1963.)

J. G. Holland (1958) and Jerison and his co-workers (1964, 1965) analysed the data in terms of *observing response*, or observing behaviour. They also regarded the vigilance task as a decision-making task, but they considered that the import-ant decision was whether or not to observe the display. (See Mackworth, 1970.)

The term *arousal* in its connotation of a state of the central nervous system is almost synonymous with the term vigilance. Changes in the level of arousal and in the probability of an arousal response to a signal have been discussed by many authors. Sharpless and Jasper (1956) were the first to discuss this in detail (see chapter 4).

Haider, Spong and Lindsley (1964) showed that missed signals coincided with decreased amplitude of the *evoked response* to the repetitive events of the task. The thesis of this book is that the vigilance decrement is related to habituation of the neural responses to the repetitive or continuous background events of the task. The detection of a signal will tend to reverse this habituation. The neural response may be thought of as an observing response, and it will be enhanced when the subject is expecting a signal to occur (Walter *et al.*, 1964).

Mackworth's experiments outlined the problem and investigated some of the variables. It was clear that a task could make too few demands on the operator, and that such tasks might be common in life. People might be carrying out dull jobs at a level of accuracy considerably below the maximum ability. Later investigators have added to the number of variables that are important, and have also considerably broadened the base of the kind of tasks that will show a temporal decrement. Chapter 2 describes more active tasks which appear to suffer from the same temporal changes.

Fiske and Maddi (1961) elaborated on the theme that variations in stimulation contribute to the normal development and functioning of organisms. Moreover, such varied experience is sought out for its own sake. Conversely, the monotonous task is often disliked, unless some other form of varied stimulation, such as talking or music, can be added. They considered that the impact of a stimulus depends on its variation or novelty, its intensity and its meaningfulness. Similar descriptions of the arousing properties of a stimulus have been given by Berlyne (1960) (see p. 84). Fiske and Maddi distinguished carefully between the impact of a stimulus and levels of arousal or activation produced by drive, time of day and other intrinsic or extrinsic factors not related to the particular stimulus. Their eight propositions outlined in detail the theoretical concepts of arousal. In the same book Fiske (p. 106–44) discussed vigilance and restricted stimulation in terms of the activation hypothesis. Other published reviews of the subject include Broadbent (1958) who interpreted the data in terms of a blocking theory, suggesting that attention automatically turned away from the task on hand when continuous attention was required for prolonged performance; Frankmann and Adams (1962) summarized the findings in terms of an arousal hypothesis, and W. E. Scott (1966) did the same, extending his thesis to monotonous tasks other than vigilance.

While the original work was mainly concerned with the detection of brief signals, the field was soon broadened to include reaction time to signals that were easy to detect, or remained visible until detected. Buck (1966) discussed the question of whether these tasks represented the same change as that found in signal detection tasks, and concluded that they did.

Unpublished reviews of the vigilance field have been prepared by McGrath, Harabedian and Buckner (1959), and T. H. Scott (1957). *Vigilance, A Symposium* by Buckner and McGrath (1963) covered most of the field as seen in 1961; and in 1965 *Human Factors* published a special issue on the subject (vol. 7, no. 2, pp. 93–183).

It is hoped that the theoretical discussion of the data presented in this book will make it clear that the various theories – inhibition, expectancy, arousal and possibly distraction – may find their places in a composite description. The brain is a very complex organ. It represents the result of millions of years of evolution and adaptation to constantly changing environments. It controls the interaction of a highly complex organism with a widely variable environment. The more our environment is man-made, the more unpredictable it becomes, because the laws of nature become more complex as they relate to more complex organisms. Our understanding of the frontier between neurology and psychology is as yet in its infancy. Thus any description of an area on this frontier must be highly tentative. If this description suggests future lines of experiment it will have served its purpose.

Summary

The vigilance task was originally designed to simulate a watch-keeping task. It presented a highly irregular series of 'wanted' signals, which were slight changes in a regular series of 'unwanted' or background events. The operator was isolated as far as possible from all other environmental variety, and received no information about his performance. Under these circumstances, a rapid decrease in the probability that a signal would be detected was found between the first and second half-hour of the task. This decrement in performance could be prevented by knowledge of results, amphetamine, or alternation of watch-keepers.

Theoretical explanations of the decrement have been given in terms of inhibition, changes in expectancy and habituation of the neural evoked and arousal responses. These three terms are by no means mutually exclusive. Habituation may be due to inhibition of the neural response to a stimulus that is not expected to require an overt response. Moreover, changes in the expectancy that an event will be a signal may lead to changes in the criterion of the subject. Changes in the neural responses may represent changes in attention, or 'observing response' made in relation to the incoming stimulus.

2 Other Tasks Showing Temporal Decrement

How far are the changes found in vigilance tasks unique, dependent on the particular aspects of the task such as rare and irregular signals, too little for the monitor to do and so on? It was pointed out by Broadbent (1958) that deterioration in performance had been found in a number of tasks that required considerable activity on the part of the operator. Moreover this deterioration did not appear to be a consequence of response fatigue or inhibition, but rather to be dependent on the monotony of the stimulus situation, which required continuous attention and decisions of a fairly simple nature. An experiment by Donchin and Lindsley (1966) has demonstrated that there are definite changes on the sensory side in a repetitive task requiring responses to every stimulus. They found that there was a correlation between the reaction time to a flash and the amplitude of the potential evoked by the flash. The reaction time was increased and the amplitude of the potential decreased as the task continued. They concluded from the nature of the changes that there was a reduction in the alerting properties of the stimulus as the task continued. This appears to be related to habituation (see chapter 5). J. F. Mackworth (1964) has shown that temporal changes in these active tasks follow the same exponential course as changes in sensitivity in a particular vigilance task.

Tracking Tasks

A tracking task is one in which the subject is required to make adjustments to controls in response to irregular movements in the stimulus pattern. Since the subject can see the result of his actions, there is usually considerable improvement in performance with practice. Deterioration in performance may only be revealed by improvements resulting from rest pauses. The difference between the level of performance at the end of a series of trials and the level at the beginning of the next series is then a measure of the amount of deterioration in performance that had occurred in the first series as a result of continued activity. While it was often thought that this deterioration was a result of the responses – that is, there was response-generated inhibition which dissipated during the rest – there is evidence that this is not the case, and that the deterioration is in fact on the sensory side. Adams (1955) examined the effect of activity during the rest pause on performance with the pursuit rotor. In this task the subject has to keep a stylus in contact with a metal plate on a revolving disc. The measure of performance is the time on target. Marked improvement is found after a brief rest. Adams found, however, that if the subject had to spend his rest watching someone else doing the task, his performance in the second period was not as good as if he had rested completely. While watching, the subject had to press a button when the active operator was on target. Rosenquist (1965) showed that although this active watching impeded recovery it did not entirely prevent it. Performance following nine minutes of watching was better than performance immediately after the initial session. Most of the recovery, however, appeared to be due to the absence of attention to the stimulus rather than absence of the response. Moreover, in this experiment tracking was initially carried out by the right hand and finally by the left hand, so that response inhibition if any must have been a central phenomenon (see also Catalano, 1967; Catalano and Whalen, 1967a and b; see p. 110).

Eysenck and Thompson (1966) studied the effect of a second task on performance in this pursuit rotor task. The second task required a discriminative response to high and low auditory tones. Performance was better without the second task, but there was an interaction between distraction and change in performance during the five minute session. In the simple task, time on target in the final minute was less than in the initial

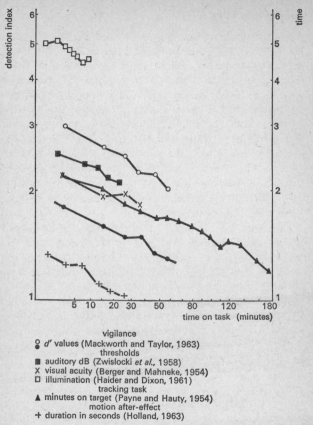

Figure 2 Log performance values as a function of the square root of time on task. (Zwislocki *et al.*, 1958) ; attenuation in decibels re. arbitrary reference level/10. (Berger and Mahneke, 1954) ; visual acuity (sum of three *S*s). (From J. F. Mackworth, 1964, p. 213)

minute, but the opposite change was found when the distracting task also required attention. Here there was an improvement during the session. The distracting task did not interfere with learning the rotor task since after a ten minute rest all groups were the same. These results suggest that division of attention interferes with perception but not with registration into long term memory (Mackworth, 1970).

Another tracking task was studied in detail by Payne and Hauty (1954, 1955) and Hauty and Payne (1955). In this task the subject continually adjusted four controls in order to keep four pointers in the centres of their respective dials. Subjects were tested for several hours. The initial improvement due to practice reached a plateau after 20 minutes and then performance began to decline. The results were recorded as time on target. Figure 2 shows that the course of the deterioration in performance followed the same exponential course as the decrement in detectability of signals on the continuous clock. The fact that decrement is most rapid at the beginning of the task suggests that it is due to habituation rather than to fatigue or response inhibition.

This task provides some feedback to the subject, because he can see the mismatch between his pointers and the null position. It does not, however, indicate to him if his attention has wandered. Hauty and Payne (1955) examined the effect of adding extra *knowledge of results* to this task. A tone or a light indicated that all the pointers were correctly aligned. It was found that performance was best with the tone and intermediate with the light, but the lines showed parallel trends after the first hour. It is probable that the alerting effect of the extra information will become less as the task continues.

Drugs had a marked effect on performance in this task. With amphetamine, performance continued to improve during the first two hours, but then showed a downward trend. With benadryl hyoscine there was maximum decrement in the first four hours. Final stabilization of performance reached a level dependent on the condition, with amphetamine giving the highest level and hyoscine the lowest. Performance following a fifteen minute *rest* after four hours work was somewhat improved but this improvement dissipated after ten minutes of further work (see chapter 8).

Thus this tracking task shows many of the characteristics of vigilance tasks – namely, exponential deterioration of performance with a final stable level of performance, improvement by knowledge of results, amphetamine and a rest pause, and more rapid deterioration with hyoscine. In common with vigilance tasks it requires continuous attention to a highly repetitive stimulus situation. Hence it is probable that the deterioration has a common cause, possibly due to a reduction in the neural response to the repetitive stimuli.

Sidall and Anderson (1955) examined a different kind of tracking task. The subject had to keep the target aligned by cranking a handwheel at a fast and constant speed of seventy-five r.p.m. The time on target decreased linearly with the duration of the session, being 27, 22, 16 and 10 minutes in the successive thirty-minute periods of the task. It is probable that in this task there was muscular fatigue as well as stimulus monotony, resulting in the linear decrease.

Yet another form of tracking task was studied by Haider and Dixon (1961). In this the manual response was reduced to pressing a button. Two spots of light differing in intensity by 0·05 log units were continuously increasing in brightness. By pressing a button the subject could dim the spots, and he was instructed to keep them at a level at which he could just see one spot but not the other. It was found that there was an increase in the level of brightness that the subject chose to maintain as the time of testing increased up to fourteen minutes. The results are shown in Figure 2. The measure was an 'integrated score' that decreased as the threshold increased. The authors pointed out that this change probably resembles the changes found in a vigilance task. These results could have been due to a genuine increase in threshold, to an increased reaction time or to an increased reluctance to make a response.

Driving is a task that requires continuous tracking. Few studies have investigated the actual driving situation, but several have tested drivers before and after long periods of driving. Jones, Flinn and Hammond (1941) found deterioration in such tests as speed of tapping, reaction co-ordination time, body sway, manual steadiness, vigilance reaction time and critical flicker fusion, after ten hours' driving. Since all these tests are quite different from changes in performance during a monotonous task, Herbert and Jaynes (1964) used tests which involved manoeuvres with the truck itself, and found significant changes correlated with hours of driving.

These manoeuvres involved complicated and accurate parking or driving in reverse and so on. Brown, Tickner and Simmonds (1966) tested drivers at 3-hour intervals during 13 hours' continuous driving. The tests consisted in repeated trips around a standard circuit. In this case driving appeared to facilitate performance. It is possible that the discrepancy between these results is due to the fact that in one case the tested activities were highly overlearned, while in the other they were not. Prolonged performance in a monotonous task may interfere with the ability to make decisions at a fairly high cortical level but not with automatic activity.

Reaction Time Tasks

Reaction times have been shown to increase with continuous testing, especially when no feedback is given to the subject (Figure 3). This increase may take the form of increases in the number and duration of the longer reaction times, with no change in the distribution of the shorter reaction times. Bills (1931, 1937) called these longer reaction times 'blocks', which were defined by him as twice the mean response time. He examined the speed at which colours could be named. The response key produced the next stimulus, so that this was a self-paced task. Similar results have been found with the five-choice task when self-paced (Broadbent, 1953). Bertelson and Joffe (1963) also studied a self-paced task, with four choices. They found that there was a marked increase in longer reaction times over the first 5 minutes, with no further change. Reaction times increased over about eight responses up to the 'block' and then immediately fell to the normal level. There was also an increase in errors up to the block. It was as if the block represented a brief rest which re-established performance. Broadbent (1958) suggested that these blocks might also be occurring in a vigilance task, and that signals occurring during the block might fail to be detected.

The five-choice task has been extensively studied under various conditions, as it has proved very informative. There are five lights, and as each comes on the subject has to tap the

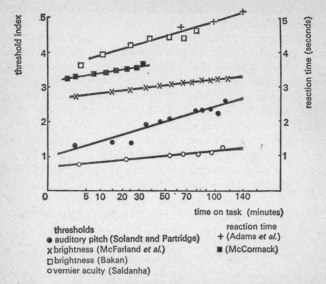

Figure 3 Changes in thresholds and reaction time as a function of the square root of time on watch. *Thresholds*: Solandt and Partridge (1945): range of discrimination cycles per second d/20 McFarland *et al.* (1942): log $\triangle$ *I* (Photons). Bakan (1955): brightness limen in foot-lamberts × 10. Saldanha (1955): vernier acuity, mean error in 0·001 inch. *Reaction time*: Mc-Cormack (1960): RT × 10. Adams, Stenson and Humes (1961). (From J. F. Mackworth, 1964, p. 214)

appropriate contact. The task can be given in two ways, either self-paced, so that each new light comes on when the previous response is made, or machine paced, when the lights come on in a random sequence at a steady pace. With the self-paced task three measures can be obtained: the number of correct and incorrect responses per unit of time, and the number of latencies that exceed a certain duration, e.g., $1\frac{1}{2}$ seconds. With the machine-paced task only one score is obtained, the number of correct responses per unit of time. Broadbent (1958) found that if the machine-paced task was given at a speed that represented the mean latency found in the unpaced task, there was a deterioration in correct responses as time on task increased.

The results of various environmental stresses on this task are discussed in chapter 7.

Singleton (1953) described a task in which the subjects had to move a lever in one of four directions, depending on which one of four lights was lit. The relation between the position of the light and the direction in which the control had to be moved was varied, being either the same, the opposite, or inclined at 90°. The task was self-paced, and each trial consisted of sixty-four responses. Except for the first trial, there was an increase in the time required to make a decision and to begin to move the lever. There was very little change in movement time, indicating that the slowing of response was due to a decision process and not to physical fatigue. The increase in response time was proportional to the difficulty of the decision, being about 3–4 per cent between halves of trials.

Mental Tracking

In the above tasks there is a considerable element of motor response, and it was for this reason that the decrement was considered to be due to response inhibition. Poulton (1960) devised a task in which the response was a verbal expression of the result of a process of mental tracking. Subjects had to keep track of the changes in repeated series of auditory digits, one digit being changed in each successive series. Poulton argued that there should be an optimal level of performance in a task which gave the operator neither too much nor too little to do. The most active and difficult task required the subjects to call out the new digit after each series (C1, see Figure 4). The easiest tasks required only detection of new sixes (C3 and C4). In each of these three tasks there was reminiscence between the first two sessions, and a decrement during the second session. The task of medium difficulty (C2) showed a steady improvement during and between the first two sessions, and it was not until the third and fourth sessions that reminiscence and decrement appeared. These data illustrate that:

1. Performance in a mental tracking task may resemble that in a physical one, in that there may be a hidden decrement

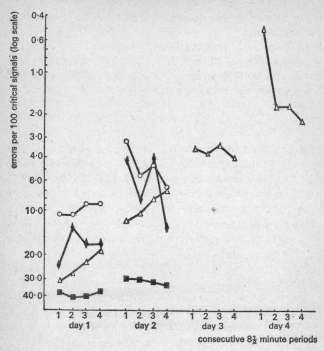

Figure 4 Mental tracking task. Trends within and between days for the four main experimental conditions. Means are based upon the following number of observations: ■, C1 all new : 128 responses from each of twelve subjects. △, C2 only position 6: sixteen responses from each of forty-eight subjects on days 1 and 2, and from each of twenty-four subjects on days 3 and 4. O, C3 only 6s: sixteen responses from each of twenty-four subjects. ◆, C4 only new 6s in position 6: two responses from each of twelve subjects (from Poulton, 1960, p. 133)

masked by learning during a session, but revealed by improvement over a rest pause.

2. Such a hidden decrement may become apparent in a second session when learning is reduced, and it may appear in a task which is very difficult or in one which is very simple. In an

intermediate task the decrement may be delayed to a later stage of learning.

3. In the most difficult condition, a response had to be made after each series of digits. This might be regarded as a forced-choice task, and therefore it would seem that the decrement could not be due to a change in criterion.

Threshold Changes

The concept of the threshold is much less secure today than it used to be since it has become clear that detection depends partly on the criterion of the subject. Thus changes found in continuous measurements of threshold do not necessarily represent changes in sensitivity. They are, however, of interest in demonstrating that such changes in apparent sensitivity may occur in circumstances in which the probability of a signal is high.

Visual sensitivity for brightness discrimination was examined by McFarland, Holway, and Hurvich (1942), who tested subjects every 30 seconds in sessions lasting for 2 to 4 hours. There was an increase in the brightness difference which the subjects were willing to accept as a good match as the session continued (Figure 3). This increase in apparent threshold was most rapid at the beginning of the session. Such a change is to be expected if the background level of neurological 'noise' is increasing due to reduced alpha blocking (see chapter 5).

McFarland *et al.* showed that if the subjects were given a brief rest with conversation or movement every half-hour, there was an improvement in sensitivity. They suggested that an increased blood supply to the brain might be an important factor. All these observations suggest that this is a phenomenon related to arousal.

Bakan (1955) tested visual sensitivity at random intervals during 90 minutes. One of two lights increased in brightness until a difference between the two was detected. This series of changes was repeated twenty-four times an hour, thus resembling a vigilance task rather than a direct measurement of threshold. The results are shown in Figure 3. As before, the increase in threshold appears to be linear with regard to the square root of time on task. (See also Haider and Dixon, p. 34).

Berger and Mahneke (1954) tested the visual acuity of three subjects for Landolt Rings. Figure 2 shows that there was a decline in acuity during 30 minutes of continuous testing.

Zuercher (1965) also employed a threshold task in a vigilance situation. A light blinked once a second, and occasionally blinked at a brighter level. If this was not detected, signals were repeated at five-second intervals at an increasing level of brightness. There were five signals in each 12 minutes of a 60 minute session. The mean detection level for the control group increased during the first 48 minutes, but improved slightly during the last 12 minutes. There were two experimental groups, one of which talked to the experimenter during the final period, while the other group was asked to move and stretch during the final period. Both these groups showed a final level of detection which was better than the initial level. These results with a vigilance task confirm those found by McFarland *et al.* in that the increase in threshold could be dissipated by exercise or conversation. Again changes in arousal appear to be the main factor leading to a deterioration in threshold.

Auditory Changes

Solandt and Partridge (1946) measured pitch discrimination thresholds every ten minutes during 2-hour sessions spent listening for sonar returns. They found that forty-eight out of eighty-one subjects showed an increased range of discrimination as the session proceeded. These data are shown in Figure 3. O'Hanlon, Schmidt and Baker (1965) followed up this experiment by examining the ability of subjects to detect in which direction the pitch of a signal was changing. No change was found between tests given before and after a 90-minute watch, but an improvement was found between the first and second sessions.

Zwislocki, Maire, Feldman and Rubin (1958) tested the

absolute auditory threshold, in periods of five minutes with rest intervals of 1–2 minutes, and found that there was a deterioration during a session of five test periods, but improvement from session to session. When a new group of subjects were offered rewards for improvement and were told after each test period how they had performed and chatted with the experimenter, the intra-session deterioration was eliminated, and the inter-session improvement increased. Thus, here again the standard effects of knowledge of results and conversation during the rest period are seen.

Improvements in the ability of the subject to detect an auditory signal, and improvements in his auditory threshold with practice have been demonstrated in a number of studies. Elliott (1957) presented tone pulses against a background of noise. The pulse was repeated at a higher level at each successive 30 seconds. He found a steady lowering of the threshold over three weeks of testing. He found that on the average effective thresholds during a test ranged from 1 to 8 dB above the alerted threshold, with a mean of about 4 dB. The improvement appeared to be related to the weaker signals. The moments when the effective threshold reached the very high levels of 10 dB above normal occurred about 5–10 per cent of the time. It is possible that these periods represent periods of drowsiness which may occur during a vigilance task (chapter 4). The effective threshold measurements were given five times an hour so that subjects theoretically only perceived five signals an hour, since the increasing series of pulses was stopped as soon as the subject responded to one.

Wallis and Samuel (1961) presented an auditory threshold task together with a visual radar task. In the auditory task the pulses increased every 4 seconds until a response was given. Ten such series were given in an hour, together with ten radar signals. When the test was continued for three hours without a break, the subjects showed a deterioration in detection in both modes during the second hour, while in the third hour they showed an improvement in radar detection at the expense of a further deterioration in the auditory task. However, when 15 minute breaks in the radar task were introduced, consisting of exercises in navigational computation and plotting, performance at both tasks was maintained at a high level throughout. However, this level was not as high as alerted performance, that is, detection when the subject has been warned that a signal will occur.

Gettys (1964) also found a deterioration in threshold during an 80 minute test, even when the subject was alerted just before the test was given. He presented twenty-four pairs of noise pulses every minute. Forty times in the 80 minutes the second member of each pair was increased in loudness until the subject responded. The alerting signal was a light that was turned off for 0·5 seconds either immediately before the threshold test or 5 seconds before it. In one condition there was no alerting signal; in another there was an alerting signal before every threshold test. The subject was urged to adopt a conservative criterion, only responding when he was nearly sure that there was a signal. It was found that there was an increase in threshold during the session. This increase was the same whether alerting signals were given or not. Thresholds tested after an alerting signal were lower than those tested without an alerting signal, but the difference between the two conditions was the same at all points of the task. The median number of false alarms was zero, so clearly the subjects were indeed adopting a cautious criterion. Thus the deterioration in performance took place even when the subject could easily localize the signal in time and was presumably reasonably aroused by the alerting signal. Such a change in performance might be expected if the subject was becoming habituated to the repetitive noise pulses.

Other Monotonous Tasks

McBain (1961) studied a task in which the subjects were required to print a series of fourteen letters. They had to repeat the series throughout a 42-minute session, at a rate paced by movement of the paper. If they recognized that they had made an error, they were required to start the series again and to signal the error by pressing a foot switch. The author reported that errors increased with time on task. This decrement did not appear to be affected by highly variable noise, although the noise acted equally throughout the session to reduce errors.

A somewhat similar task was reported by Chapanis (1964). Subjects were required to punch random digits into a teletype. It was found that there was considerable improvement in speed over sessions. In the later sessions a decrement during the session began to appear.

Perception

The use of the square root of time as an ordinant for Figures 2 and 3 was suggested by Taylor, who found that changes in many situations were proportional to the square root of time on task (Taylor, 1966). In this paper he summarized work on various experiments as follows:

(a) The decay of the figural after-effect was exponential, with a time constant proportional to the square root of the length of the inspection time.

(b) For motion after-effect, the product of the time constant and the initial after-effect varied with the square root of the inspection period.

An experiment reported by H. C. Holland (1963) is also relevant here. He carried out a massed series of measurements of the after-effect of the rotating spiral. Subjects inspected the spiral for 30-second periods, each inspection period following immediately after the after-effect from the previous period had disappeared. Figure 2 shows that the durations of the successive after-effects were inversely proportional to the square root of the total time spent on inspection. Holland found that the 'inhibition' generated by massed practice was dissipated by rest, trial spacing, bell-ringing and amphetamine, while it was increased by amytal. Thus this decline in after-effect of seen motion with repeated stimulation resembles the various active and passive tasks discussed here.

(*c*) *Movement neutralization.* Taylor found that when subjects were required to keep a disc rotating at what they judged to be a constant speed, they in fact increased the speed continuously. This increase was exponentially related to the square root of time.

(*d*) *Visibility of a partially stabilized retinal* and

(*e*) *effect of a contour on visibility of a nearby light spot* also showed a relationship to the square root of the inspection time.

(*f*) *Fluctuations of perceptual organization.* This section of Taylor's report is perhaps most relevant to theories of vigilance behaviour. When subjects were paying attention to an un-varying stimulus pattern, two phases of perception were observed. For a short while, up to a minute, no change in the percept was mentioned. After this, transformations of the percept were reported at such a rate that the cumulative number of transformations increased as the square root of time of inspection. For instance, a regular series of bleeps occurring four times a second was presented. The subject was led to expect that there would be a rhythm in the series and was asked to record what she heard by long or short dashes. The subject was, in effect, making false judgements, since no such differentiation was in fact occurring. Thus, a decrease in the number of changes reported might represent the same phenomenon as that found in a vigilance task when a decrease in false responses occurs. Other stimuli included reversing figures and repetitive verbal material. Again changes were reported where, in fact, there were none.

It may be possible that the transformations of the percept represent attempts by the subject to recognize and classify material which cannot be readily classified in terms of existing models. A model of the stimulus is being constructed, and eventually the stimulus can be classified in terms of its own model and thus the struggle to fit the stimulus to pre-existing models may die down. The vigilance decrement can under certain circumstances be represented by exponential changes or changes proportional to the square root of time on task. Figures 2 and 3 show vigilance changes in detectability and reaction time. Taylor (1966) also showed that data reported by Wiener, Poock and Steele (1964) indicated that the criterion of the subjects might change according to the square root of time on task (Mackworth, 1970). As described in chapter 9, changes in criterion or sensitivity may depend in a complicated way on the actual changes in arousal response or evoked potential.

Summary

The data presented in this chapter show that a decrement in performance, expressed as changes in sensitivity, criterion, speed or accuracy, may be found in a very wide variety of tasks. In each case the changes appear to be related to the square root of time on task. It has also been found that after-effects and purely subjective transformations show a relationship with the square root of total inspection time. It can, therefore, be concluded that the vigilance decrement may not be due solely to temporal uncertainty, but may be a particular example of a wide-spread phenomenon involving decrease of neural reactivity to continued or repetitive stimulation. Such a decrease is regarded as a particular example of habituation of physiological responses. Changes in physiological measures attributed to habituation may also follow a negatively accelerated course, but the available data are very variable.

3 The Evoked Potential

When a stimulus change reaches the neural system, it produces a series of rapid changes in potential. Studies with human subjects usually measure these potentials with electrodes placed on the scalp in various positions. The scalp recording is a resultant of many processes in the brain, and it would appear that the successive changes in potential represent the passage of the neural response through the various neural pathways. Thus, the successive components of the evoked potential do not respond as a unit to changes in the stimulus. For instance, visually evoked responses in humans show components, occurring about 100 milliseconds after the stimulus, which are responsive to changes in the physical characteristics of the stimulus. The physical properties of the stimulus reaching the sensory nerves may be affected by the 'observing response' of the subject, which would alter the portion of the retina receiving the stimulus, the diameter of the pupil, and the tension of the ear muscles, both external and middle ear. Later components of the evoked potential (around 200–300 milliseconds) are related to the cognitive aspects of the stimulus. A late negative wave may be considerably increased when the subject is drowsy. Finally, a very late phase may represent alert attending for a stimulus known to be contingent on a warning stimulus. This expectancy wave may last for a second or so.

Relation between the Physical Aspects of the Stimulus and the Evoked Potential

Wicke, Donchin and Lindsley (1964) examined the relation between the duration and luminance of a flash and the visual evoked potential, measured over the visual cortical area in humans. They found that with constant duration the latency, amplitude and waveform of the evoked response varied with the luminance. As the luminance was reduced, the amplitude of the first diphasic component (latency 80–120 milliseconds) was reduced until this component disappeared. At the same time, the amplitude of the second component (latency 175–210 milliseconds) increased and reached a maximum when the first diphasic component disappeared. With further reduction in luminance, this second component also diminished, and a long positive wave of 200–400 milliseconds developed near threshold. In a second experiment, the luminance and duration of the flashes were varied reciprocally so that their product was constant. The waveforms of the evoked potentials remained relatively constant in shape when the product was kept constant, even though considerable variations in luminance were employed. The latency, however, increased as the luminance was decreased. It was concluded that the wave form and amplitude of the evoked potential were directly related to the apparent brightness of the stimulus, while the latency was related only to the luminance of the flash.

Donchin and Lindsley (1965) studied the relation between the evoked response and the inter-flash interval between two flashes. The luminance and duration of the two flashes determined the interval at which the first flash began to be masked by the second. Between the masking phase and the stage at which two flashes were clearly seen there was an enhancement phase. In this phase the evoked response was approximately a linear sum of the responses to the two flashes presented alone. In the masking range, the evoked response to the pair was the same as the response evoked by the second flash alone.

Diamond (1964) found that the latency of the visual evoked potential was inversely proportional to the logarithm of the intensity of the flash stimulus. White and Eason (1966) summarized detailed studies on the relation between stimulus variations and the evoked potentials. They varied the flash intensity and the background luminance independently. The first component (C1, 100 milliseconds after the flash) increased in amplitude as the intensity of the flash increased, and decreased as the intensity of the background increased. It was also found that, when two flashes were given at varying intervals of temporal separation, the perceived brightness varied inversely with the duration of the inter-flash interval. They suggested that C2 was related to scotopic visual activity, because it was only present with the lower background intensities, while C1 and C3 were related to photopic activity. C3 appeared to be particularly related to background intensity, and it was suggested that this might be due to photosensitization. Colour studies showed that C1 was most responsive to green and C3 to red.

When series of flashes were presented at a rate of thirty flashes per second, there was a direct relationship between the number of flashes that were reported and the number of components in the evoked potential. The authors concluded that if a stimulus was seen by the subject, an evoked potential would be recorded.

White and Eason also found that the amplitude of the late components was larger with a structured visual stimulus than with a *ganzfeld* or unstructured visual field. A similar finding was reported by Lifshitz (1966), who tested subjects with slides that were either in focus or not. He found that the evoked response to the focused slides showed a maximal late negative wave beginning 200–300 milliseconds after the stimulus. This late negative wave was absent when the slides were defocused, indicating that the late response was related to the meaningfulness or information content of the stimulus.

Eason, Oden and White (1967) examined the relationship between the visual evoked potential and the site of retinal stimulation. The early components of the evoked potential were increased as the stimulus approached the fovea, but the later components were increased with more peripheral stimulation. Latency showed a U-shaped relation with the distance from the fovea, being minimal at 15–30° positions, especially with the later components. Minimal reaction times were found with a central stimulus and also with the stimulus at 15–20°. Thus, there was a fairly close relation between reaction time and latency of the evoked potential. The relation between reaction time and amplitude of the evoked potential was less clear-cut (see p. 53).

The evoked potential is considerably reduced if stimuli are given too close together. Abraham and Marsh (1966) examined the relation between the rates of repetitive clicks and the amplitude of evoked potentials recorded from implanted electrodes in unanaesthetized cats. The rates varied from four stimuli per second to one in 10 seconds, and it was found that the amplitude of the evoked potential recorded from the auditory cortex was reduced as the rate of stimulation increased. No such relation was found in the cochlear nucleus (Figure 5). The late components of cutaneous evoked potentials recorded in the hypothalamus of anaesthetized cats are reduced if a stimulus occurs within 6 seconds after the previous one, and are completely eliminated if the interval is less than half a second (Abrahams and Langworth, 1967). There may well be a connexion between these findings and the marked reduction in detections found in a vigilance task when the background event rate is increased (Mackworth, 1970).

The Cognitive Aspects of the Evoked Response

John (1967) described data indicating that information about the stimulus is carried in the temporal pattern of the neural changes produced by the stimulus. The shape of the evoked potential is related to the physical and cognitive aspects of the stimulus. The cognitive aspects include the expectancy or set of the subject as to the nature of the stimulus. For instance, John (1967, p. 410) quoted an unpublished experiment by Ruchkin, Torda and Negrin which showed that wave shapes resembling those normally evoked by presentation of a particular geometric form could be obtained in response to illumination of an empty field if the subject imagined that the form was present.

There seems to be adequate evidence that under certain circumstances the amplitude, shape and latency of the evoked potential may vary. One factor of importance is the *amount of*

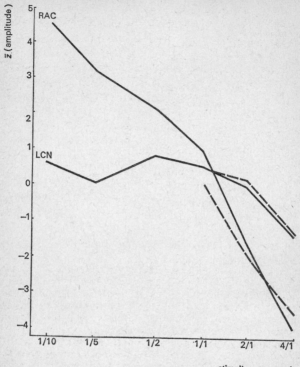

Figure 5 Mean z-scores of peak-to-peak amplitude of auditory evoked potentials as a function of presenting rate for three cats run in all experimental conditions. Solid lines indicate single-frequency conditions: dotted lines indicate alternating-frequency conditions, plotted at their over-all presenting rate. RAC = Right Auditory Cortex, LCN = Left Cochlear Nucleus (from Abraham and Marsh, 1966, p. 193)

attention being paid to the stimulus. When a subject is attending to a stimulus, the amplitude of the potential evoked by that stimulus is larger than it is when he is not paying attention to the stimulus. (García-Austt, 1963; see p. 57, and Figures 11a and b; Hernández-Peón, Jouvet and Scherrer, 1957; Spong, Haider, and Lindsley, 1965; see Figure 6). Such shifts

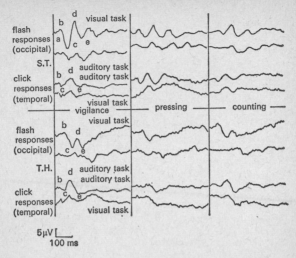

Figure 6 Computer-averaged cortical evoked potentials obtained from two subjects S.T. and T.H. in response to flashes and clicks. The potentials were recorded from the occipital and temporal areas while the subjects performed visual and auditory tasks under three experimental conditions: vigilance, key-pressing and counting. Flashes alternated with clicks throughout. Each trace is the averaged evoked response to 300 stimuli. Analysis time, 500 milliseconds. In the upper left-hand section, the major peaks and troughs of the visual and auditory evoked responses are identified by letters a to e; the amplitude of the wave defined by c-d-e- is the principal differentiating criterion. Recordings: right occipital and temporal areas to left ear; negativity upward (from Spong, Haider and Lindsley, 1965, p. 396)

of attention can be related to the interference effect of one task upon another. Broadbent and Gregory (1963a) showed that the addition of a secondary task resulted in a marked reduction in the sensitivity of the subject for the signal as measured by d' (see Mackworth, 1970). Moreover, the effect of attention on the evoked potential can be demonstrated even when the different kinds of stimuli are being presented in the same sensory mode. Donchin and Cohen (1967) presented

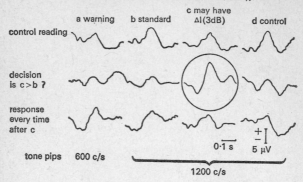

Figure 7 Slow responses evoked by auditory stimuli and recorded from the vertex. Tone pips at about 70 decibels hearing level were delivered at the start of each trace. The intervals, a-b, b-c, c-d, d-a, were all 2·5 seconds. Responses to thirty-two cycles were averaged. Δ I (3 decibels) was added ten times and also subtracted ten times in the 'decision' series. Upward deflection indicates that the vertex is becoming more positive relative to the right mastoid. The band-width of the electroencephalogram was 0·3 to 35 cycles per second (from Davis, 1964, p. 182)

a flash of light superimposed upon a background that consisted of a square alternating periodically with a circle. The subject was told either to pay attention to the light or to the shapes. The stimulus to which the subject was attending elicited a potential with a considerably enhanced late component.

There is considerable evidence that the cognitive aspects of the stimulus are particularly represented in the late components of the evoked potential. John (1967, p. 254) has quoted work indicating that there are marked differences in the late components obtained during correct performance and those obtained during response failures. H. Davis (1964) showed that although routine responding to a tone did not increase the potential, as compared with no response, there was marked increase in the late positive phase when a discrimination was required (Figure 7). Sutton *et al.* (1965)

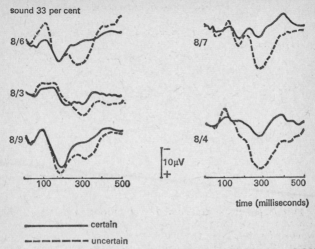

sound 33 per cent

8/6

8/7

8/3

8/9

8/4

10μV

100   300   500

100   300   500

time (milliseconds)

——————— certain

— — — — — uncertain

Figure 8 Average waveforms for certain and uncertain ($P = 0.33$) sounds for five subjects (from Sutton, Braren, John and Zubin, 1965, p. 1187)

suggested that the early stage in the evoked potential reflects processes involved in perception of the stimuli, while the later components reflect those processes related to its significance. Sutton *et al.* presented clicks and flashes and found that when the subjects were uncertain as to the nature of the expected stimulus, the amplitude of the late positive deflection (300 milliseconds) was greater than when the stimulus mode was known beforehand. (Figure 8).

There is also evidence that the speed and accuracy of a motor response are related to the qualities of the evoked response. Morell (1965) found an increase in amplitude of the late components of the evoked response as the response speed increased. Donchin and Lindsley (1966) demonstrated that faster reaction times were associated with greater amplitude of visual evoked potentials. Moreover, when verbal knowledge of results was given, the reaction times were shorter, and the amplitude of the evoked potential was larger (Figure 9).

Wilkinson and Morlock (1967) examined the auditory

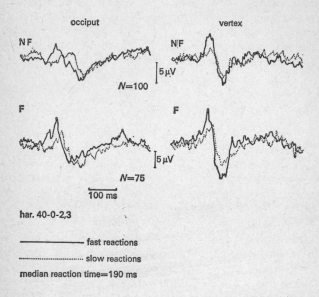

Figure 9 Solid lines: average evoked potentials to light flash when reaction time faster than median; dotted lines: same, when reaction time slower than median reaction time. F = Feedback (from Donchin and Lindsley, 1966, p. 220)

evoked potential in relation to a motor response. They found no relation between the reaction time and the amplitude of the evoked potential in brief trials of 100 seconds' duration, though in a more prolonged test they had found a positive relation between amplitude and speed of reaction. They concluded that the difference was due to the length of the testing period, and suggested that in short tests the subject might be in a state of over-arousal, which would impair performance. In the short test they found that when a response was required to the clicks, there was an increase in amplitude of the early components of the evoked potential, and a reduction in the second or late negative wave, with a latency of 260 milliseconds, and also a large-amplitude late wave appeared. This had a latency of 350–450 milliseconds and might have been a 'motor' potential. When the incentive was increased, all these changes were emphasized. They pointed out that these changes related to increased alertness were the opposite of those found in a vigilance task (see p. 68).

The Contingent Negative Variation (C N V) or Expectancy (E) Wave

Walter (1964a and b; also Walter *et al.*, 1964) showed that the evoked potential following a stimulus might be succeeded by a secondary negative wave which might last for some time, if the first event was signalling that a second event would occur at a definite time interval after the first. He presented a series of flashes to human subjects. The surface-negative components of the evoked potential showed rapid habituation, though the positive wave habituated more slowly. When habituation was complete, a click was introduced after each flash. The subject had to respond to the click by pressing a button. Thus when the flash arrived, the subject prepared himself to press the button after the click which he knew would follow. Under these circumstances, the secondary negative response to the flash, the warning signal, increased and lasted until the click appeared. The potential evoked by the click itself gradually attenuated. When the probability of a click following a flash was reduced to 0·5 the C N V was attenuated, while the response to the click was increased. The subject now had to delay his decision to press the button until the click actually occurred. Walter pointed out that the C N V was a non-specific response, and that such non-specific responses usually showed habituation.

Irwin, Knott, McAdam and Rebert (1966) showed that the C N V was larger when a response was required to the second stimulus, when a painful shock was anticipated, for more difficult detection, and for a greater response effort (see also Hillyard and Galambos, 1967 and Rebert *et al.*, 1967).

Habituation of the Evoked Potential

Thompson and Spencer (1966) presented a comprehensive account of work on habituation of evoked potentials and concluded that 'There is as yet no consistent agreement regarding the occurrence of habituation in sensory systems of the waking brain.' This warning must be borne in mind in considering the following account. On the other hand White and Eason (1966), in a series of studies on the occipital evoked potential produced by light without contours, commented 'The well-established habituation of response to repetitive stimulation is undoubtedly related to subjective factors such as attention, vigilance, level of activation and meaningfulness of the stimuli' (p. 11). Brazier (1964) pointed out that the method of time-locking or averaging has certain disadvantages, one of which is that small changes occurring between one response and the next are concealed. When habituation is being studied, this drawback may be serious. A second factor that may obscure habituation of the evoked potential is the strength of the stimulus. Responses to very intense stimuli may not habituate, and workers often use such stimuli in examining the evoked potential in order to obtain a good record.

Since it is being suggested that habituation of the evoked potential is related to the vigilance decrement, a fairly full description of the data which demonstrate habituation is given. There is considerable evidence that changes in the evoked potential may occur as the stimulus is repeated. The nature of these changes is more complex (see Thompson, 1967, chapter 15). The evoked potential has a number of components which vary differentially with physical and cognitive aspects of the stimulus, as well as with the position of the electrodes, and the state of the subject. These components may represent quite different aspects of brain function. For instance, Rose and Lindsley (1965) have shown that the long-latency negative wave, which may represent the non-specific response, is present in the kitten at four days old. This response is blocked by lesions of the superior colliculus and of pretectal regions of the midbrain. The early components of the evoked potential may represent the specific response to the stimulus, and do not appear in the kitten until 10–15 days of age. The specific response is blocked by lesions of the lateral geniculate. These two components may be compared with the tonic and phasic types of arousal response and may therefore be found to behave differently in relation to stimulus repetition. Thompson and Shaw (1965) have shown that the non-specific posterior association responses in cats do not habituate and increase as the level of activation is decreased. Thus, it is clear that interpretation of changes in the evoked potentials requires considerable caution and much more investigation. It should also be noted that the use of bright flashes and loud clicks may result in complete absence of habituation.

Perry and Copenhaver (1965) reported that habituation of the evoked response to a repetitive flash was greater when the peripheral retina was stimulated than when the fovea was stimulated (Figure 10). It has been mentioned (p. 48) that the early components of the evoked potential become smaller as the stimulus moves towards the peripheral retina. Thus it would appear that peripheral stimulation resulted in a subjectively less bright stimulus.

García-Austt (1963) summarized studies on implanted electrodes in awake rats and guinea-pigs, saying that 'the changes produced by habituation and distraction upon evoked potentials occurred all along the visual pathway from the optic nerve up to the cerebral cortex' (p. 83). Habituation of the visual evoked potential was independent of the background EEG activity, and could occur during light sleep. García-Austt, Bogacz and Vanzulli (1964) found that, at the beginning of a session with human subjects, the amplitude of the visual evoked potential was reduced by distraction, such as a tone, a peripheral flash or even mental calculation. When, however, habituation of the visual evoked potential had occurred, peripheral stimuli increased the amplitude (dis-

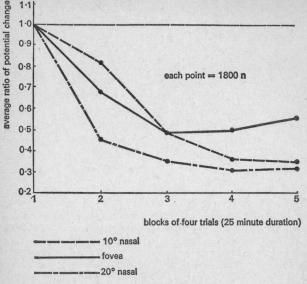

Figure 10 Habituation of evoked potentials to three retinal locations of stimulus (from Perry and Copenhaver, 1965, p. 1212)

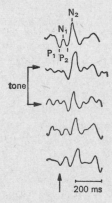

Figure 11a Visual evoked response changes induced by distraction. Averaging of forty responses in each record. The vertical arrow indicates the stimulus delivered at a frequency of 1 per second (from García-Austt, Bogacz and Vanzulli, 1964, p. 137)

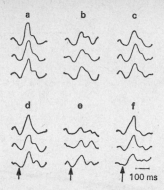

Figure 11b Visual evoked response changes induced by interference with another photic stimulation. Each record – the average of forty responses – is obtained by stimulating the central retina at 1 per second. Vertical arrows indicate the stimulus. (a) Three successive records, before habituation; (b) effects of interference by stimulating the peripheral retina with an extra flash delivered at random; (c) immediately after discontinuance of extra stimulation; (d) the same as in (a); (e) three successive records after habituation; (f) the same as in (b). (From García-Austt, Bogacz and Vanzulli, 1964, p. 137)

habituation) (see Figures 11a and b). A change from regular to random or discontinuous series of flashes also increased the amplitude (Figure 12). They found that the evoked potential showed marked fluctuations after habituation had occurred. Garcia-Austt (1963) reported a similar effect with the auditory evoked potential of the awake guinea pig measured with an electrode implanted near the round window. Habituation of 'cochlear microphonics' and of the 'action potentials' of the auditory nerve were found, even when the middle ear bones were removed. A high intensity repetitive flash reduced the auditory nerve potential before habituation had occurred (distraction); after habituation, the presence of an observer in front of the cage increased the auditory response (dishabituation).

Fox (1964) examined habituation of the visual evoked potential in monkeys. Atropine, which produced maximum

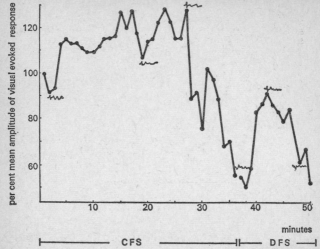

Figure 12 Visual evoked response changes during photic habituation. Ordinates, 40 per cent peak-to-peak amplitude of the rapid initial variation N1-P2. Each point is the averaging of forty responses. Abscissae, time in minutes. CFS., continuous flicker stimulation at 1 per second. DFS., discontinuance flicker stimulation (forty flashes at 1 per second separated by a 40-second darkness period). The amplitude increases at onset to decrease rapidly after twenty-five minutes. The change from CFS. to DFS. produces an increase in amplitude which is not maintained (rehabituation) (from Macadar *et al.,* 1963, p. 318)

pupilary dilation, did not prevent habituation, which was rapid and pronounced with a regular series of flashes. It was even more rapid when the monkeys generated the flashes themselves, thus removing any element of surprise. This finding emphasizes how important to habituation is the agreement between an event and what is expected. When the flashes were given at random time intervals, no habituation occurred in the 50 seconds of the test (Figure 13).

Haider, Spong and Lindsley (1964) (see Figures 14a and b) showed that there was habituation of the potential evoked by the repetitive visual background events of a vigilance task. Missed signals were related to reduced potentials produced

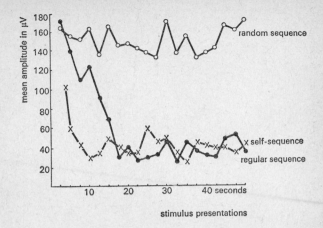

Figure 13 Differences in amplitude habituation for three different temporal patterns of stimulus presentation over groups of twenty stimuli separated by 30 minutes of darkness. (The self-sequence is self-initiated in this experiment.) (From Fox, 1964, p. 229)

both by the background events and by the signal events.

Thompson and Spencer (1966) and Thompson (1967) summarized the data on habituation. They mentioned that some authors failed to obtain habituation when the eye was atropinized and an artificial pupil was used (Fernandez-Guardiola, Roldán, Fanjul and Castells, 1961). It is possible that changes in pupil size may play a part in reduction of the evoked potential during a vigilance task.

A number of studies have suggested that the *late components* of the evoked potential may be particularly concerned with decision or cognitive aspects of the stimulus. Habituation may represent a decision that the stimulus is fully conformable to expectation, and that it is not significant. Thus, changes in the late components of the response may be particularly important in habituation. Brazier (1964) studied visual responses recorded in the centre median of an unanaesthetized cat and found that the second wave, with a latency of about 100 milliseconds, gradually disappeared with repetition of the

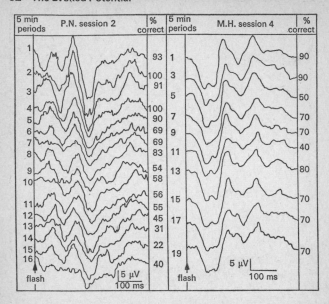

Figure 14a Computer-averaged evoked potentials for 100 non-signal stimuli presented during successive 5-minute periods of a visual vigilance task, together with the percentages of randomly interspersed signal stimuli correctly detected during the same time periods. Recordings : occipital to vertex reference ; negativity upward. Subjects P.N. and M.H. (from Haider, Spong and Lindsley, 1964, p. 181)

flash leaving the initial response unchanged. Bogacz, Vanzulli and García-Austt (1962) also found that, after habituation, responses became simplified, with disappearance of the late response. Domino and Corssen (1964) also reported habituation of the visual evoked response, especially in the late waves three and four.

The Auditory Evoked Response

Several workers have reported habituation of the auditory evoked potential at the cochlear nucleus (see Dunlop, Webster

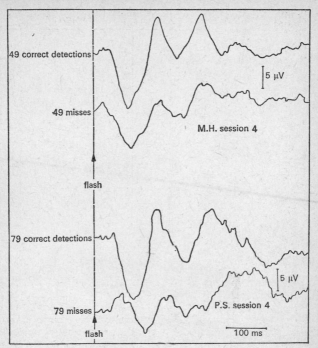

Figure 14b Computer-averaged evoked-potentials for equal numbers of detected and missed signal stimuli by subjects m.h. and p.s. Both subjects show evoked-responses of reduced amplitude to the missed signals (from Haider, Spong and Lindsley, 1964, p. 181)

and Rodger, 1966, who quote Hernández-Peón and Scherrer, 1955; Galambos, Sheatz and Vernier, 1956; and Marsh, McCarthy, Sheatz and Galambos, 1961; Worden and Marsh, 1963). García-Austt (1963) reported habituation of the auditory nerve response in active guinea-pigs, even when the ear bones had been removed. Marsh and Worden (1963) found no consistent changes in the cochlear nucleus of cats, but there was habituation of the auditory evoked potential in the cortex of the cats when they were in an alerted condition. No such change occurred when the cats were not alerted (Figures 15a, b and c). In the auditory cortex, the amplitude of the evoked potential was greater during sleep than when the animal was awake.

Dunlop, Webster and Rodger (1966) found habituation of the response to clicks in unanaesthetized cats at the cochlear nucleus, the inferior colliculus and the medial geniculate body. In the first two regions, habituation was complete within 20

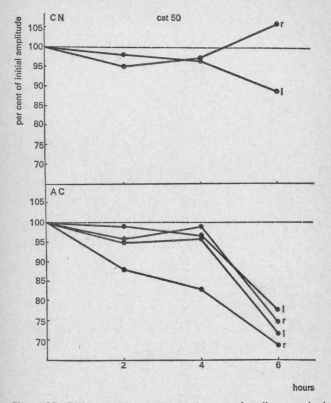

Figure 15a Differences in amplitude changes of auditory evoked potentials of one cat, in the alerted condition, measured at cochlear nucleus (CN) and the auditory cortex (AC). The inconsistency between right and left CN, and the contrasting consistence of amplitude decrement in simultaneous recordings from AC are typical (from Marsh and Worden, 1964, p. 688)

minutes, but in the medial geniculate body, there was much greater habituation that continued over the 90 minutes of the experiment.

Bogacz, Vanzulli and García-Austt (1962) reported habituation of the auditory evoked potential in man (see Figure 16).

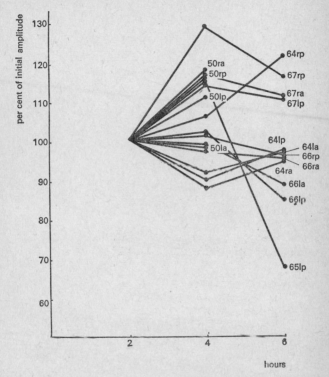

Figure 15b For the non-alerted condition, amplitude changes at auditory cortex are plotted as a percentage of the amplitude of the 2-hour non-alerted sample. (A non-alerted sample was not available at 0 hours). For cat 50, no non-alerted sample was taken at 6 hours. Animal numbers are followed by letters indicating left (l) or right (r) cortex, and anterior (a) or posterior (p) electrode. The direction of amplitude change here contrasts sharply with that for the immediately following alerted samples (from Marsh and Worden, 1964, p. 688)

Wilkinson, Morlock and Williams (1966) found evidence of two kinds of change in the auditory evoked potential of humans during a vigilance task (Figure 17). There was no change in the first negative wave, but the second positive

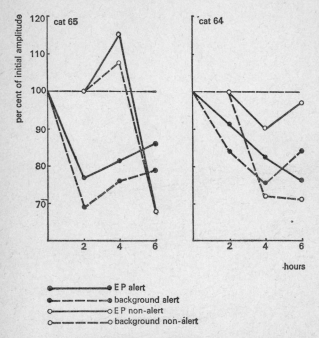

Figure 15c Changes of amplitude of cortical background activity and auditory evoked potentials (EPs) plotted as percentage of initial amplitude in two cats. For each cat, alerted data are plotted in solid black dots, while non-alerted data are plotted with circles. Peak to peak amplitude of evoked potentials (solid line) represent for each point, the mean of a sample of thirty-five responses. For background activity (dashed line) each point represents the mean amplitude of 100–130 measurements spread every 2·5 seconds through the sample. For both the non-alerted and the alerted conditions the tendency for evoked potentials and background amplitude to covary is clear (from Marsh and Worden, 1964, p. 688)

potential decreased, and the second negative potential increased in amplitude as the task progressed. These potentials were measured at the vertex. It was found that the probability

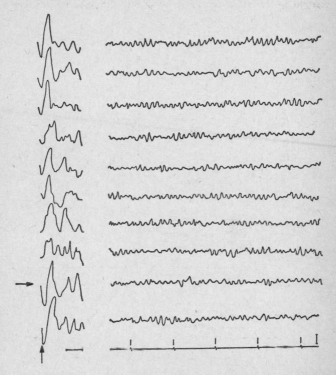

Figure 16 Changes of auditory evoked responses during wakeful-ness. On the left, the averaging of forty responses in each record. On the right, length of 5-second EEG, sample corresponding to each one of the explorations. The vertical arrow indicates the stimulus delivered at a frequency of 1 per second. The AER regularly diminishes in amplitude during habituation, the same level being always observed in the EEG. At the horizontal arrow dehabituation was provoked by interference with flashes at different frequency of clicks. The AER increased in amplitude, again without variation of the EEG (from Bogacz, Vanzulli and García-Austt, 1962, p. 246)

that a signal would be reported was correlated with the latency of the first negative potential change, and with the amplitude of the second negative potential, but not with changes in the positive potential. They suggested that the

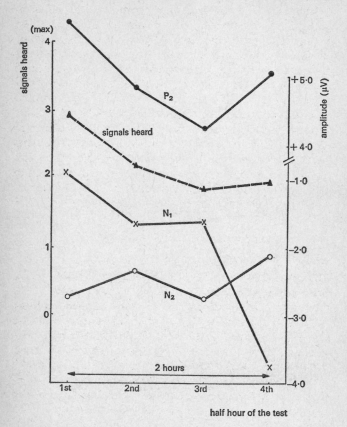

Figure 17 Amplitude of first negative (N_1), second positive (P_2) and second negative (N_2) components of the auditory evoked cortical response (ECR) and the associated level of signal detection in an auditory vigilance task (from Wilkinson, Morlock and Williams, 1966, p. 221)

changes were characteristic of those found in changes in the level of arousal, since Williams, Tepas and Morlock (1962) had found an increase in the amplitude of N_2 in the transition from waking to sleep.

Wilkinson and Morlock (1967) examined the effect of requiring a response to an irregular click (p. 53). The requirement of a response resulted in an increase in amplitude of the early wave and a decrease in the second negative wave, as compared with the same stimulus input when no response was required. This result was, therefore, the converse of that found in the vigilance task. In the vigilance task, a decline in attention as the task progressed was associated with an increase in the late negative wave, while, in the other experiment, an increase in attention due to the need to respond resulted in a decrease in the second negative wave. This second negative wave (latency 265 milliseconds measured at the vertex) behaved like the non-specific posterior association responses studied by Thompson, Denny and Smith (1966, see below).

Relation of the Evoked Potential to Arousal

Thompson (1967, Ch. 15) has discussed in detail the difference between the primary and association evoked potentials. The former are directly related to the amount of attention being paid to the stimulus, and to the level of arousal, while the latter have an inverse relation to these factors. Measurements of scalp potentials may contain both these elements. Shaw and Thompson (1964a and b) and Thompson and Shaw (1965) have studied the posterior cortical association responses of the cat by the use of indwelling electrodes. The amplitude of the responses *decreased* as the degree of the orienting response increased. Thompson, Denny and Smith (1966) found that activation of the frontal association response field of the cerebral cortex of the cat enhanced the later (N1 and P2) components of the primary evoked sensory response, an effect that normally accompanies behavioural attending. At the same time, the non-specific posterior responses were inhibited.

A number of workers have found that there is an increase in the amplitude of the late negative wave of the auditory evoked potential with the onset of drowsiness or sleep. (Bogacz, Vanzulli and García-Austt, 1962; Rapin, 1964; Weitzman and Kremen, 1965; Williams, Morlock, Morlock and Lubin, 1964). A similar change was found by Wilkinson, Morlock and Williams (1966) in a vigilance task (see p. 66). Ornitz *et al.*, (1967) suggested that sleep onset may be associated with increased facilitation or decreased inhibition, and that the late negative wave may be the measure of a sensory pathway parallel to that of direct sensation. This parallel sensory pathway would seem to be similar to that of the non-specific association responses described by Thompson (1967). Eason, Oden and White (1967) found that small weak visual stimuli triggered rhythmic responses which had the same frequency as the alpha rhythm characteristic of the subject. They suggested that the rhythmic responses shared the same mechanism as the regular background activity. Kooi, Bagchi and Jordan (1964) reported that the amplitude of the visual evoked potential was diminished during drowsiness, but increased again during sleep. García-Austt (1963) found that the late components of the visual evoked potential increased during sleep, but still showed habituation with repetition.

A highly significant correlation between increased amplitude of the visual evoked potential and increased activity at all frequencies of the background E E G in man was found by Rodin *et al.*, (1965). Levonian (1966) found, however, that visual evoked potentials showed maximal amplitude immediately before low-frequency alpha, while the responses preceding high-frequency alpha were attenuated and opposite in sign.

Spontaneous background activity can inhibit the evoked potential, especially the late components. Abrahams and Langworth (1967) studied the potential evoked in the hypothalamus of anaesthetized cats by cutaneous shocks or light flashes. The potential was considerably larger when the stimulus was delivered in a period of little background activity than when low-amplitude background activity was present. Spontaneous spikes occurred once or twice a second, and reduced or completely inhibited the late negative waves of evoked potentials produced by stimulation shortly after a spike. Sometimes the positive wave was exaggerated by the presence of a spike. It has been mentioned (pp. 47, 49) that one evoked response inhibits another that follows too closely, and it would seem that a spontaneous change in potential can have the same inhibiting effect. These findings are reminiscent of the psychological refractory period (see Sanders, 1967).

It is clear that there is a relation between the evoked potential, especially the late components, and the nature of the spontaneous background rhythm. It is a basic concept of signal detection theory that the signal 'rides' on the noise. The recorded evoked potential is usually extracted by a computer from the background 'noise' by averaging potentials from the known temporal points at which the signal was given. Can the brain do the same when it does not know when a signal actually occurred? It would seem dangerous to imagine that the information received by the brain about a signal resembles the information that the computer can extract.

Summary

By the use of averaging techniques, it has proved possible to record the neural response to a stimulus as an evoked potential. This consists of a series of rapid changes in potential, and it has been found that the different components of the response vary independently with changing conditions. The late components of the response may be particularly sensitive to the cognitive attributes of the stimulus, and also to the level of arousal. Behavioural attending leads to an increase of the specific evoked responses and a decrease in the non-specific long-latency responses, especially the late negative wave.

Repetition of the stimulus may lead to habituation of the evoked response, with a decrease in amplitude, especially of the late positive response. Habituation is most marked when the repetitive stimulus is comparatively weak, and when no overt response or discrimination is required. With the onset of drowsiness, there may be an increase in the amplitude of the late negative wave. Both these changes, a decrease in the late positive and an increase in the late negative waves, have been recorded during vigilance tasks.

An 'observing response' or 'act of attention' may therefore increase the amplitude of the evoked response to the events of a vigilance task, both signals and non-signals. An increase in the rate of events decreases the size of the evoked potential just as such an increased rate decreases the probability of signal detection (see Mackworth, 1970). As a result of decreased amplitude of the evoked response to the background events of the task, arising from habituation, fewer neural events may reach the criterial level for response (see chapter 5). An increase in the non-specific response (or late negative wave) related to a decrease in arousal may lead to a decrease in sensitivity.

4 Physiological Arousal and Activation

The term 'vigilance' was taken from Head (1926) to imply that both mind and body were in a state of readiness. This state of readiness appears to be related to the physiological state which has been called activation, arousal, energy mobilization or excitation (see Duffy, 1962). Whether the decrement in a vigilance task is, in fact, directly related to a change in the level of arousal, as defined by physiological measures, is discussed in chapters 5 and 9. The present chapter presents a brief outline of the physiological changes that are considered to be evidence of changes in arousal.

Arousal may be considered from two aspects. There is the over-all or *background level* that characterizes the state of the organism. This varies according to the time of day, the level of emotion, drive or motivation, the genetic constitution of the individual and many other factors. Secondly, there is the arousal response to a particular stimulus, which may include the whole environment. The arousal response is often known as the *orienting response*, since it may be accompanied by an active search, including turning towards the stimulus (Sokolov, 1963).

Both of these aspects, the general level of arousal, and the arousal response, are extremely complex and involve widespread changes in the organism. The most important cause of the arousal response is the novelty or unexpectedness of the stimulus. It therefore follows that as the stimulus is repeated, the arousal response decreases. This decrease represents *habituation* of the arousal response. Habituation has been defined as 'a decrease in response resulting from repetition of the stimulus' (Harris, 1943). This definition could also be applied to the vigilance decrement. Hernández-Peón (1960) enlarged the definition to 'an innate response'. The major question is therefore: Is the decrease in the required, or learned response in a vigilance task connected with, or caused by, a decrease in innate responses such as the arousal response or the evoked potential?

This chapter is devoted to an outline of the present knowledge about arousal, with particular reference to the arousal response. A decrease in the arousal response to a particular series of stimuli is not necessarily related to an overall decrease in the general level of arousal.

Cannon (1936) described how the body is prepared for 'fight or flight' by the autonomic nervous system. The sympathetic system induces changes in almost every part of the body. It increases and redistributes the blood flow, widens the pupil, alters heart rate and respiration rate and depth, and releases extra blood sugar. Other changes whose immediate function is not so clear include sweating, correlated with decreased skin resistance, and erection of hairs. At the same time, there may be increased tension in the muscles, preparatory to action. Thus the body is in a state of *activation*. The parasympathetic nervous system has in general the opposite effect to that of the sympathetic so that activation as a general state may involve inhibition of the parasympathetic (see Duffy, 1962).

Certain changes in the electrical rhythms of the brain, as measured by the electroencephalograph (EEG) have also been found to be characteristic of alert attention. The history of these researches has been described by Lindsley (1960). Lindsley (1952) considered eight different levels of physiological states, ranging from excited emotion to death. He correlated these levels with changes in behaviour and in the EEG. The two highest levels are characterized by fast, desynchronized low-amplitude waves. The appearance of these waves is known as activation, desynchronization, EEG arousal or the alpha blocking reaction (Moruzzi and Magoun, 1949). These authors showed that stimulation of the reticular activating system (RAS) produced the desynchronization pattern in the cortex. Normally, the RAS is activated by incoming stimuli through the non-specific pathways and by impulses coming from the cortex. When the subject is in an alert but resting state, the E E G commonly shows the alpha rhythm. This consists of relatively high-amplitude regular waves with a mean frequency of ten cycles a second. The terms 'alpha blocking reaction' or 'alpha block' refer to the replacement of the alpha rhythm by the activated desynchronized pattern as a result of stimulation. The large slow rhythmic changes passing over the cortex during sleep can also be replaced by the desynchronized response as a result of stimulation, and Sharpless and Jasper (1956) defined this change as the arousal reaction (Figure 18, p. 92).

In addition to the reticular system, Podvoll and Goodman (1967) found that high-frequency activity in the thalamus of cats was directly proportional to the level of behavioural arousal, even when the cortical E E G was dissassociated from behaviour by atropine. Arousal responses in the cochlear nucleus and inferior colliculus did not habituate with repetition, but those found in the medial geniculate were associated with behavioural arousal and did habituate.

Electrical stimulation of the amygdala and of the posterior suprasylvian gyrus of cats also leads to both behavioural and neural arousal changes, which habituate on repetition (Ursin, Wester and Ursin, 1967). After habituation, arousal can be produced by a different stimulus. The authors found that mesencephalic stimulation led to orienting behaviour even when repeated 100 times. They regarded these facts as evidence for indirect production of arousal in the cortex and direct production in the mesencephalon. Mackworth Bagshaw and Pribram (unpublished) have found that removal of the mygdalas in monkeys destroys the visual orienting response.

Stimulus Arousal The Orienting Response

While the general level of arousal may vary for a number of reasons, most of the study of arousal has centred around the response to a stimulus. When an animal is asleep, or lying quietly, a novel, unexpected stimulus will produce a syndrome that is called behavioural arousal. A stimulus which is of importance to the animal may produce many of the same changes. In the pattern of behaviour shown by a dog when his master dons a coat preparatory to taking a walk can be seen most of the features of bodily arousal. The orienting reflex or response includes both the visible behaviour such as sitting or standing up, looking around, pricking the ears and so on as well as widespread changes in the body and brain.

The orienting reflex is a non-specific reflex initiated by any qualitative change in a stimulus (Sokolov, 1963, p. 189). It increases the discriminatory power of analysers (ibid, p. 195). It has the property that it is subject to extinction or habituation on repeated presentation of the stimulus. Sokolov and his colleagues (Sokolov, 1963) have investigated this reflex in great detail. Lynn (1966) has presented a very useful summary of this work.

Sokolov suggested that the following changes take place during the orienting reflex:

(1) Changes in the sensitivity of peripheral analysers

Decreases in thresholds for one mode of stimuli may be produced by stimuli of another mode. For instance, Watkins (1966) found that detectability of a tonal signal in a specified observation interval was increased when a light was simultaneously intensified. Such changes may be partly due to muscular changes, such as wider opening of the eye, fixating the source of the stimulus, turning the ear or head towards the stimulus, or increased tension of the ear muscles and so on.

(2) EEG changes

The desynchronization pattern or alpha block has two forms. There is the *non-specific* reaction, which is prolonged, and spreads widely throughout the cortex, but soon ceases to occur when the stimulus is repeated. There is also the *specific* reaction, which is limited to the part of the cortex that is specific for the particular sense organ. Thus the response to visual stimuli is found over the occipital area. This response is quite brief, not more than a second or so, but it continues to occur long after the non-specific reaction ceases to be provoked by a repeated stimulus. These two types of arousal reaction were also described by Sharpless and Jasper (1956) as tonic and phasic activation patterns respectively. The arousal reaction may reduce the spontaneous activity of the brain, so that the direct neural response to the incoming stimulus, the evoked potential, may be more clearly demarcated against a lower neural noise level. Kogan (1960) reported that cortical desynchronization during a sensory stimulus was accompanied by a decrease in threshold in the primary receiving area, together with an increase in threshold in other cortical areas.

(3) Autonomic changes

(a) The galvanic skin response (GSR). The level of skin conductance rises with the level of arousal. Three types of change in skin conductance have been examined extensively: (i) The basal level shows slow downward drifts when a subject sits quietly, and is often regarded as a measure of the over-all level of arousal or activation. Woodworth and Schlosberg (1954) and Duffy (1962) give full accounts of the use of this and other physiological measures of activation. (ii) The GSR occurs in response to a stimulus. It may have a fairly long latency, about a second or more, which may be shortened when the subject is required to make a discrimination (Surwillo, 1967b). (iii) Spontaneous GSR also occur in resting subjects, and their frequency can be used to distinguish different types of individuals. (See p. 121).

(b) Heart rate. The heart rate is regarded by Malmo (1959) as an important measure of activation level. In animals it increases with increased drive or emotion, and there may also be an increased stroke output. The increase in heart rate is due to sympathetic action. There is, however, a very complicated system of reflexes associated with the heart, and in humans the orienting reflex is often characterized by a marked fall in heart rate.

(c) Vascular reactions. Sokolov paid a great deal of attention to vascular reactions because they allowed him to distinguish

between the orienting reflex and the defence reaction. In the orienting reflex there is contraction of the blood vessels of the finger and dilation of the cephalic vessels, while with the defence reaction there is constriction in both areas. Sokolov pointed out that the cephalic vasodilation has the property of increasing the blood flow to the principal analysers. Kakolewski and Takeo (1967) found that the tonic arousal response is associated with a rise in arterial pressure which soon habituates. No such rise is found with the more stable brief phasic response.

(d) Respiration rate. This tends to increase with anxiety and to slow down with relaxation and sleep. Like the heart rate, the orienting reflex may produce temporary inhibition of respiration.

(e) Pupillary dilation. (See p. 85).

(4) Muscle tone

Arousal is characterized by an increase in muscle tone, as measured by the muscle potentials in inactive muscles.

The orienting reaction is not quite the same as the 'fight or flight' mechanism. It has added to it certain changes, often mediated by the parasympathetic, which are related to a concentration upon determining the nature of the stimulus, and it does not cover the same range of stimuli, since it can be distinguished from the defence reflex, which is a response to very strong stimuli and does not habituate.

When an unknown or unexpected stimulus arrives, the first questions are 'What is it, where is it?' Only when it is identified does the question become 'What shall I do about it?' First a signal must be detected, then it must be classified, and finally a decision must be made as to what kind of response would be most suitable.

Over-all Level of Arousal or Activation

Duffy (1962, p. 227) concluded that individuals show con-sistent differences in activation at different times and in different situations. Individuals also differ in the patterns of activation of various kinds of physiological responses (Lacey, 1950; 1967; Wenger, 1941; see chapter 6). Eysenck (1963) suggested that introverts were more aroused than extraverts and could therefore perform better in tasks offering little stimulation than could extraverts.

Apart from genetic factors and the stimulating qualities of a particular situation, levels of activation may be related to the emotional state of the subject (Lindsley, 1960) and his motivation in regard to the situation. There may also be a diurnal rhythm of arousal level, which is different for different people. The place of drive and motivation in behaviour has been discussed in detail by Stellar (1960). Clearly drive or motivated behaviour involves much more than simple arousal, since such behaviour is directed towards satisfying a particular need. Stellar defined drive as the intensity of motivated behaviour and suggested that the direction and pattern of behaviour are organized through the hypothalamus.

Malmo (1959) suggested that drive, without the steering component, was identical in principle with activation or arousal. It has been proposed that there is a U-shaped relation between the level of arousal and performance. At very high levels of arousal, performance may deteriorate (Duffy, 1957; Freeman, 1940; Stennett, 1957). A curvilinear relation between stimulation of the rostral brain stem of rats and performance was found by Wilson and Radloff (1967). The number of trials to criterion on two variable-reward schedules was lowest with the medium level of stimulation, and increased with both no electrical stimulation and with an increased intensity. Since stimulation of the reticular system is considered to be equivalent to arousal, the authors interpreted their results as 'documenting the empirical validity of the arousal-performance function'

It is doubtful whether drive and arousal can be completely equated. It has been pointed out by Sokolov (1963) that there are differences between the orienting and the defence reflex. As the intensity of the stimulus increases, the defence reflex replaces the orienting reflex. The defence reflex is very stable, while the orienting reflex shows rapid habituation as the stimulus is repeated. Similarly, physiological drives produce very stable responses. A pigeon will peck for hours at a high rate in order to obtain a small ration of food (Skinner, 1938). The arousal response to a repeated stimulus rapidly disappears.

The Definition of Arousal

No definition of arousal is fully satisfactory. The body has only a limited number of autonomic responses available, and these responses may occur as a result of a number of different patterns of activity within the brain. If arousal is defined as awareness or attention to the environment, then the desynchronization changes in the brain are not related monotonically to arousal, since these changes may be found in the drowsy state, as well as in paradoxical or rapid eye-movement sleep (Morell, 1966; Podvoll and Goodman, 1967). In the latter case, the brain may be active, in dreaming, but consciousness, or attention to the outside environment, is minimal. Scott (1966) defined the activation dimension as running from convulsions at the upper end to delirium and coma at the lower, and suggested that sleep was to be found on a different dimension. Hernández Peón and Sterman (1966) have summarized the evidence for an active inhibitory hypnogenic system, and Thompson (1967) has pointed out that sleep and waking may involve all the brain regions (ibid, p. 475). The state of 'readiness to detect and respond' to changes in the environment is only related to the middle range of the hypothetical arousal continuum, the range from alert attention to light sleep. In general, this is the range that will concern us in this book, although hyper-arousal, where arousal is postulated to be too high for optimal performance, has been invoked by several authors.

In terms of the background rhythms of the E E G, four levels can be distinguished in the range that we are considering (Lindsley, 1960; Oswald, 1962).

1. *Fully alert*. Desynchronized low-amplitude fast frequency waves are continuous, and stimuli produce no change.

2. *Alert but relaxed*. The alpha rhythm is continuous, but is replaced by desynchronization when novel stimuli are given.

3. *Drowsy*. The desynchronized rhythm reappears, with occasional spindle bursts and slow high-amplitude waves. The response to a repetitive stimulus may be a burst of alpha rhythm (Morell, 1966, see page 95).

4. *Sleep*. Large irregular slow waves are interspersed with occasional K-complexes. The latter are provoked by stimuli that are not strong enough to produce complete arousal. Strong stimuli produce the arousal reaction of desynchronization (Sharpless and Jasper, 1956).

It can be seen that the best definition of brain rhythms related to arousal includes both the background rhythms and the response to a stimulus. The interaction between the level of activation and habituation of the response to stimuli is complex and will be discussed later.

Duffy (1962, p. 17) has defined the level of activation as the extent of release of potential energy, as shown in the activity of a response, when all variables except one are held constant. She described how Wilder (1957; see Duffy, 1962, p. 31) found a curvilinear or inverted U-shaped relation between the effects of pharmacological agents and stimulation on blood pressure, foot temperature and blood sugar. When the initial level of the dependent variable was high, stimulation might produce a decrease.

Fiske and Maddi (1961, p. 21) defined activation as the state of a catalytic and energizing mechanism in the central nervous system and arousal as the manifestations of activation in various parts of the organism. Thus there may be one continuum of activation in all higher organisms, but it may manifest itself in different ways, and have different causes. It would seem from these definitions that activation is not measurable, but remains a purely theoretical construct, invented to salvage the appealingly simple idea of a single continuum. The authors suggested that activation refers to the state of excitation of a brain structure, probably the reticular system. The EEG pattern has not, however, proved to be monotonically related to a common-sense definition of alertness, and therefore it might be more satisfactory to speak of reticular activation, rather than the more general term of activation, with its wider implications.

Varying levels of reactivity of neural, autonomic and voluntary responses have been demonstrated, but no universally accepted definition of the meaning of arousal or activation has been produced. It may be that this is due to the complexity of the brain. There is a highly complex system of interacting processes of excitation and inhibition, and activity of the reticular and thalamic systems is only one part of the pattern. Emotions, motivation and drive have not been unequivocally demonstrated to be related to some single factor of arousal that can be independently defined. The concept of arousal, nevertheless, remains a stimulating and useful one, provided that it is realized that any particular measure of arousal is not necessarily a measure of an over-all state.

Lacey (1967) has discussed the relationship between the various measures of arousal, and has concluded that electrocortical, autonomic and behavioural arousal may be considered to be different forms of arousal, each complex in itself. In general, the three complexes occur simultaneously, but they can be separated by various means. Thus, atropine produces the theta waves characteristic of sleep, but the animal remains alert and responsive. Conversely, cortical desynchronization can be produced by stimulation of the midbrain reticular formation in an animal with nearly complete bilateral lesions of the posterior hypothalamus, but such animals cannot be behaviourally aroused.

Both Lacey (1967) and Sokolov (1963) have shown that the vasomotor components of the orienting response or attentive observation of the environment show a marked parasympathetic change, in contrast to the sympathetic changes characteristic of the defence reflex or emotional response thought to be characteristic of high arousal.

The Nature and Significance of the Stimulus

It has been pointed out that a definition of the neural level of activation should include both the resting EEG pattern and the response to stimuli. The nature and history of the stimulus in relation to the subject must also be known. An important factor is the *novelty* of the stimulus for the subject. The response to a repeated stimulus tends to decrease. This is the process of habituation (see chapter 5). Several authors have suggested that the brain constructs models of external events, and these models contain not only the spatial factors of an event, but also its temporal characteristics. (See Lynn, 1966, for a summary of such theories.) Any event whch does not adequately match the model of what is expected to occur will produce an orienting reflex. The neural effects of an event which matches the model will be inhibited. There may be an interaction between the level of alertness and the effect of a stimulus. Thus, the inhibitory effect of the model may be less discriminating at lower levels of alertness, so that small diffcrences are not detected. On the other hand, the inhibitory effect may disappear in sleep, so that habituation disappears (Johnson and Lubin, 1967). Tranquillizers may increase the rate of habituation of the alpha block (Tissot and Bovet, 1967).

The qualities of the stimulus that are related to the orienting response (OR) have been described by Sokolov (1963) and summarized by Lynn (1966). (See also Mackworth, 1970, and Thompson and Spencer, 1966.)

1. *Novelty*. This may be absolute or relative. A stimulus may be completely ncw, or merely new in the context in which it is presented. As a subject grows older and more experienced, there are fewer stimuli of the first kind, and more of the second kind.

2. *Changes in the stimulus* may include changes in pitch, intensity, shape, duration or changes in the temporal pattern of a series of stimuli. The omission of an expected stimulus in a regular series results in an OR. When the stimuli are presented at irregular intervals, the ORs continue much longer than with a regular pattern (Fox, 1964).

3. *Intensity*. The strength and duration of the OR is directly related to the strength of the stimulus (except perhaps at threshold level). At a certain strength, the OR is replaced by the defence reaction (see also Leavy and Greer, 1967).

4. *Significance*. (a) When a motor response is required to a stimulus which has ceased to evoke an OR, the OR returns, and is more stable than when no discrimination is required.

(b) When discrimination is required between two stimuli the OR is stronger than when no discrimination is required, and the OR increases as the discrimination becomes more difficult. Berlyne (1960; 1966; see Berlyne and Peckham, 1966, for references) has shown that complexity, uncertainty and conflict in and related to the stimulus will increase the OR as measured by duration of EEG desynchronization, or GSR. Berlyne and McDonnell (1965) found that the duration of EEG desynchronization was longer for the more complex material in two sets of similar patterns, but was not different between sets of very different patterns, even though the different sets were judged as showing considerable differences in complexity. Berlyne and Nicki (1966) found that there was a U-shaped relation between pitch and duration of alpha block, with the shortest response at 800 CS.

Lehmann, Beeler, and Fender (1965) found that the EEG pattern varied during the fluctuation of perception of stabilized retinal images. Alpha activity predominated during the fade-out of the image, while low-voltage fast waves were present, when the image was visible. They also found (Lehmann *et al.*, 1967) that when light flashes were delivered to the right eye while the left eye viewed stabilized images, there were no significant changes in the evoked potential responses to the light flashes. Thus, the changes in CNS activity level represented by the changes in the background rhythm did not affect the amplitude of the evoked potential response. When a structured target was presented to one eye and flashes to the other, the amplitude of the evoked responses to the flashes was reduced. When, however, the pattern was presented as a stabilized image, it had less effect on the amplitude of the response to the flashes. The greatest response to the flashes was found when the other eye saw a dark field. The effect of divided attention on the amplitude of the evoked potential is discussed in chapter 3.

Arousal and Memory

We are familiar with the realization that an effort of attention is necessary for memorizing, and the evanescent nature of the memory of dreams is also well recognized. Kahneman and Beatty (1966) found that the pupil dilated when material was being memorized. Dilation of the pupil has been used by many workers as a sensitive measure of the level of arousal (Hess and Polt, 1960, 1964, 1966). If the subject is asked to recall a number from long-term memory, the pupil dilates with the mental effort of recall and then quickly constricts as the recovered number is verbalized (Kahneman and Beatty, 1966).

Freedman, Hafer and Daniel (1966) examined EEG changes during learning, and compared them with those found in a control group with the same stimuli and response mode, but no possibility of learning. The task required learning the relation between auditory nonsense syllables and response keys. Any effects due to habituation should have been common to the two groups. There was no significant relation between high frequency waves and learning, but the learning groups showed significantly more alpha and fewer slow waves than the control group. These differences increased as learning progressed. The authors interpreted their results as indicating that arousal was reduced as learning progressed, while the control group increased in arousal, due to frustration. A decrease in alpha and an increase in slow waves is, however, equally compatible with a decrease in arousal.

Recall of words producing high arousal (measured by GSR) has been found to be poor immediately after presentation; but much better after 45 minutes than recall of words not associated with high arousal (Kleinsmith and Kaplan, 1963).

Registration in the Central Nervous System

Bagshaw, Kimble and Pribram (1965) suggested that the GSR was involved, not in the generation of reaction to novelty, but in the registration of novelty in the central nervous system They based this suggestion on the finding that bilateral amygdalectomy in monkeys decreased GSR reactivity, although it retarded behavioural habituation (see chapter 5 for the discussion of the theoretical processes involved in formation of a model). In monkeys with frontal ablations, EEG responses to tones or lights were normal, but GSR did not occur unless the animal moved (Grueninger et al., 1965). GSR did occur in response to shocks, but showed abnormally slow returns to normal levels. In these animals, GSR never became conditioned to tones which were paired with shock. The authors suggested that the GSR might represent mainly the rapid return of the CNS to normal levels and that this rapid return was inhibited by frontal lesions. Nishisato (1966) suggested that the GSR had a latency about one second longer than the EEG response. He reported overt reaction time was longer when measured during a GSR than when measured when the skin potential was steady. He contrasted this with the finding by Lansing, Schwartz and Lindsley (1959) that the overt reaction time was shorter when measured during an EEG response, and concluded that the GSR represented a late phase in the arousal phenomenon. Surwillo (1967a) measured the relation between GSR and frequency of the alpha rhythm (eliminating alpha blocks from the data) and found a very low positive correlation between period of EEG and GSR latency.

Nadel (1966) tested rats with cortical spreading depression induced by K Cl and found that this did not prevent habituation of exploratory activity during a session, but did prevent habituation between sessions. He interpreted these data as indicating that the cortex was not necessary for the inhibition of activity, but was necessary for the formation of a long-term model.

These data support the suggestion that the cortex is involved in the registration of experience in the form of a neural model. (See Thompson and Walker, 1963.) This may involve two stages (see p. 101). The first may be an *alerting* reaction in which the organism, as it were, says 'What's this?' It can be supposed that the brain extrapolates into the future, each actual event activating a pattern or programme of the expected next event. The incoming stimulus is compared with the activated model, and if the two patterns, incoming and stored, are noticeably different, the reticular formation is activated, and the orienting response is set in motion. The second stage is the stage of *focusing and registration* (Pribram, 1967). A new model of the pattern of events is constructed. This second stage is dependent on the frontal cortex and involves learning, especially long-term learning, which is another way of describing the formation of a model. During this stage, which may have a latency of a second or more, the pattern of arousal spreads more widely, to include the GSR and other physiological responses. The first stage may not be very sensitive, so that small discrepancies from the expected event are not noticed. Following these stages comes the process of *habituation*, as the new model is completed and reaches a high level of predictability.

Not only does ablation of the frontal cortex or amygdalectomy interfere with the second stage of registration, it has also been shown by Thompson, Denny and Smith (1966) that stimulation of the frontal association response field of the cortex of cats increases primary cortical evoked potentials and inhibits nonspecific cortical evoked potentials. These two effects can be separated by the use of drugs, suggesting that they may be due to different mechanisms. (See p. 169).

Summary and Conclusions

Under certain circumstances, an animal reacts to a stimulus with a widespread pattern of bodily changes. These include, activation of the autonomic system, mainly sympathetic, increase in muscle tension, orienting behaviour towards the stimulus, and damping down the spontaneous synchronous rhythms of the brain. A hypothetical state of arousal has been postulated to explain this generalized response to stimuli that are novel, unexpected, complex or significant. It is assumed that the arousal response results in an increased ability to detect, classify and respond appropriately to the stimulus.

In addition to the arousal response to a particular stimulus, the general level of activation of the body varies with such factors as the time of day, hunger or thirst, motivation or interest, and the level of physical activity. Individuals may show marked differences in their general level, as well as in their patterns of response. There is not necessarily a correspondence between the arousal response to a stimulus and the over-all level of arousal.

The neurological arousal response to a novel or unexpected stimulus involves the appearance of low-amplitude fast desynchronized patterns. Normally, this replaces a background of high-amplitude alpha waves characteristic of relaxed attention, and is then known as the alpha block. Reduction in the variance of the background noise level should result in an improved ability to discriminate the incoming stimulus. The warning signal used in signal detection experiments may result in a prolonged desynchronized response, so that the brain is at its most efficient to detect the following signal.

Two kinds of alpha block or E E G arousal response have been described. The generalized response is prolonged, but rapidly disappears with repetition of the stimulus. The specific response is located in the part of the cortex specific to the stimulus mode, and is brief, but occurs after many more repetitions of the stimulus than does the generalized response. Eventually, in a monotonous situation, the background alpha will itself disappear, and then the response to a stimulus may be the reappearance of alpha waves. Thus, changes in the total amount of alpha in such a situation are not necessarily monotonic.

It is important to notice that the level of arousal or the arousal response does not depend on the total amount of stimulation though it may be related to the variety, significance or complexity of the stimulation. Moreover, irrelevant stimulation may be harmful to performance due to distraction. If arousal is defined by changes in brain rhythms, then the maximum level is reached in interesting and rewarding tasks of a reasonable level of challenge. This maximum level is represented by the continuous desynchronized pattern, with no change when stimuli are presented. If arousal is measured by sympathetic changes, such as heart rate, GSR, pupil width, and so on, increases may be found with much higher intensities of stimuli, emotions or drives. These higher levels of physiological responses have been classified as the defence reflex by Sokolov (1963). U-shaped relationship between these physiological measures and performance have been found. In view of the complex nature of the patterns of response, it would be better to speak of the kind of response rather than the general term 'arousal'. The term is so widely used, however, that it cannot be avoided. The hope is that a causal relationship between one or more of the bodily changes and performance will be found. Important aspects would appear to be the neurological changes, and perhaps changes in the peripheral sense and effector organs.

5 Habituation and Neuronal Inhibition

The most important causal factor in the production of the orienting response (OR) is novelty or unexpectedness. This can be seen in the finding that the OR dies away as the stimulus is continued or repeated. For instance, Berlyne and Nicki (1966) showed that the alpha block following the onset of a tone lasted longer than a $\frac{1}{2}$-second tone, but ended before the cessation of a 3-second tone. *Habituation* is defined as a response decrement arising as a result of repeated stimulation (Harris, 1943). The response is sometimes defined as innate (Hernández-Peón, 1960) and therefore unlearned and involuntary. Otherwise, the definition could be applied to performance in a vigilance task. Habituation appears to be an active process of inhibition rather than a passive process like fatigue.

Sharpless and Jasper (1956) suggested that the decrement in vigilance tasks and other monotonous tasks was due to this process of habituation. Haider, Spong and Lindsley (1964) further suggested that the vigilance decrement might be related to habituation of the evoked potential response to the repetitive background events of the task. Evidence as to habituation of the evoked potential is somewhat conflicting (see chapter 3). The changes found in a vigilance task may, however, be related to habituation of both these neural changes, the arousal response and the evoked potential, as well as to changes in expectancy, perhaps with a concomitant change in the contingent negative variation or expectancy wave (see p. 55).

Thompson and Spencer (1966) presented a succinct account of the general laws that appear to apply to habituation. They suggested that habituation might be due to the cumulative effect of a polysynaptic low-frequency depression, and that habituation would be more rapid as more neurones intervened between stimulus and response.[1] The authors illustrated each of their statements by experiments on the hindlimb flexion reflex of the acute spinal cat. Their views can be summarized as follows:

(a) The first important statement that Thompson and Spencer made about habituation was that the decrease in response was usually a negative exponential function of the number of stimulus presentations. Thus, if the stimuli are presented at a faster rate, habituation is faster.

(b) The response recovers when the stimulus is omitted.

(c) Habituation is faster for weak stimuli, provided that discrimination is not required. However, see item (g) below.

(d) Habituation of response to one kind of stimulus may generalize to another.

(e) A different, usually strong, stimulus may lead to recovery of response to the original stimulus. Repetition of the new stimulus may lead to habituation of its effect.

All these statements deal with the habituation of stimuli to which no overt voluntary response is required. Two other findings may be added to this list:

(f) The rate of habituation depends on the regularity of the stimulus. Fox (1964) has shown that habituation of the neural response to a light flash does not occur when the flashes are irregular (Figure 13); (see also McDaniel and White, 1966).

(g) When the stimulus requires a response, or a decision as to whether or not to respond, habituation is delayed (Sokolov, 1963). In such circumstances, habituation may be slower when the discrimination is more difficult.

Habituation of the Arousal Response

Sharpless and Jasper (1956; see Figure 18) made a detailed study of habituation of the arousal reaction of the sleeping cat to a tone. The first three tones, presented at irregular inter-

1. A discussion of the relationship between these findings and vigilance data will be found in chapter 9.

vals over 15 minutes, gave neural activation responses lasting for about 3 minutes each. There was then an abrupt fall in duration of the arousal response to 30 or 15 seconds. This slowly became shorter as the tones were repeated, until by the thirtieth stimulus there was no arousal reaction. The response had become completely habituated. At this point, a different tone produced arousal, but if the original tone was

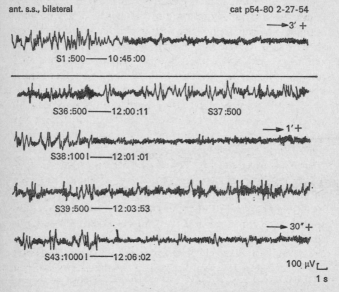

Figure 18 Cortical electrograms from the suprasylvian gyrus of a normal cat showing typical habituation of the arousal reaction to a 500 cycle tone after about thirty trials. In the first tracing the response to the first presentation of the 500 cycle tone is shown (S1:500). The solid bar shows the duration of the stimulus followed by the time in hours, minutes, and seconds (10:45:00). In the second tracing is shown the thirty-sixth and thirty-seventh trials (S36 and S37). Then a novel tone (!) of 100 cycles is presented in the thirty-eighth trial (S38:100!) followed by a repetition of the habituated tone (S39:500) and then another novel tone (S43:1·000!). The figures at the right above the EEG traces indicate the duration of the activation in each trial (from Sharpless and Jasper, 1956, p. 659)

presented after this arousal reaction had ceased, no activation occurred. They therefore suggested that the so-called disinhibition or dishabituation effect of a novel stimulus was due to the non-specific arousal that it produced. It is, however, clear that this explanation could not be relevant to the spinal cat tested by Thompson and Spencer (1966).

Sharpless and Jasper suggested that there were two kinds of arousal response: the brief *phasic* reaction, which shows slow habituation, is quickly restored by the lapse of a few minutes without a stimulus; and the sustained *tonic* reaction, which shows rapid habituation and needs 15 minutes or more of rest to be restored. They suggested that habituation of the tonic reaction was mediated by the reticular formation; it is much less specific than habituation of the phasic reaction, which they considered to originate in the diencephalon. A similar distinction has been drawn by Sokolov (1963; see p. 76).

Generalization. Sharpless and Jasper (1956) reported that when the animal had become completely habituated to a tone of 500 cycles per second, it would still give an arousal response to tones of 100 or 1,000 cycles per second. A 600 cycle-per-second tone did not, however, produce arousal. Changes in the pattern of the tonal stimulus could produce arousal, though not so effectively as changes in pitch. Corman (1967) and J. A. Williams (1963) also studied generalization. Corman presented ten repetitions of a tone at irregular intervals and found that the GSR decreased and often completely disappeared. This represented over-learning or below-zero habituation. Then a new tone was presented for five trials. The response to the new tone was less when there had been more trials with no GSR to the first tone. The reaction to the new tone was a function of the difference between the two tones. It is probable that this generalization process is important in the vigilance situation.

Habituation of the visual arousal response. García-Austt, Bogacz and Vanzulli (1961) studied the alpha blocking reaction in man occurring as a result of regular flashes of light. At first these flashes produced a continuous pattern of desynchronization, against which the evoked potentials were clearly visible. After a while, the alpha rhythm reappeared between the flashes, which were occurring every two seconds. Each flash was now followed by a very brief alpha block, the phasic reaction described above. The introduction of an extra flash produced the prolonged tonic activation response. When the series of flashes was discontinued, another prolonged tonic reaction occurred. Sometimes sleep patterns appeared after a prolonged series of flashes.

The Relation between the Arousal Response and the Overall Level of Arousal

The classic study of Sharpless and Jasper (1956) was carried out on sleeping cats, thus showing that habituation of the arousal response does occur during sleep. Oswald (1962) found that during light sleep the GSR disappeared but returned and did not habituate during medium or deep sleep. Sokolov (1963) found that previously habituated GSR would return during sleep but could habituate.

While the arousal response to visual stimuli is usually the replacement of the alpha rhythm by the desynchronized low-voltage rhythms, the opposite changes may occur, especially if the subject is drowsy, and also if the stimulus is auditory. Oswald found that if a subject was required to respond monotonously to a stimulus repeated at regular intervals, the EEG might change to that characteristic of light sleep. Then the stimulus would be followed by bursts of alpha rhythm. Sometimes short alpha responses would occur even though the subject failed to respond to the stimulus. At other times there would be no EEG response, and no overt response to the stimulus.

H. L. Williams (1964) also found that when sleep-deprived subjects were tested in a vigilance-like task, errors of omission occurred during periods of EEG theta (slow wave) activity.

Surwillo (1963) found that as the frequency of the brain

waves slowed, the reaction time to a stimple stimulus increased. There was a correlation coefficient of 0·72 between RT and brain wave period.

A study of background EEG during a task resembling a vigilance task has been reported by Morell (1966). The subjects (group R) were required to respond to a light that was presented aperiodically around a mean intersignal interval of ten seconds. The duration of the task was about twenty-five minutes. Another group of subjects (NR) were studied under the same conditions, except that no response was required to the light. It was found that two kinds of EEG background activity and response occurred. At the beginning of the session, the background activity was the alpha rhythm characteristic of alert relaxed attention. The response to the stimulus was the alpha block. Later in the session, however, a different kind of EEG pattern was found. The background was one of low-voltage random activity, with some slow waves, and the response to the stimulus was a burst of alpha rhythm. Thus in a way, this pattern was the reverse of that found at the beginning. The stimulus-produced alpha response was the longer latency and duration than the alpha block. Reaction times were significantly longer with the stimulus-provoked alpha, than with the alpha block. Throughout the latter part of the experiment there was an alternation between these two kinds of EEG patterns.

Habituation of the alpha block was found with both groups. When the alpha rhythm was present, habituation during the session was shown as a reduction in the percentage of flashes that were followed by the block. The NR group showed a greater reduction in blocking responses than the R group. Thus, there were two changes that were found during the session: (a) habituation of the alpha block, and (b) overall changes in background activity and nature of response. It was found that the occurrence of long reaction times was much more frequent when alpha was not present in the background activity but was provoked by the stimulus. Thus it appears that this pattern of background low-voltage activity was associated with a reduced readiness to respond to a signal.

Morell suggested that the alternation between the two kinds of background activity represented a homeostatic mechanism. The alpha rhythm and block pattern might be due to the excitatory function of the reticular system, while the random activity-alpha response pattern might result from reactive inhibition (see also Kreitman and Shaw, 1965).

The alpha response was observed both when the subject omitted a response and when he made a false response. Thus the pattern of the subject's response was not dependent on the alpha response, but the motor response might be triggered by an alpha response which was not itself a consequence of the light flash. This finding agrees with the concept that a false response is due to an observation of noise that is identical with an observation of noise plus the signal. In other words, there is an overlap of the distributions of noise and signal-plus-noise events in the neural system (see Green and Swets, 1966).

Johnson and Lubin (1967) examined the effect of monotonous auditory stimulation during waking and sleeping. In this experiment, no response was required to the tone. They found that all measures of the orienting response habituated when the subjects were awake; with the onset of sleep, the physiological responses increased, and there was little or no habituation during sleep.

It can be concluded that habituation of arousal responses is most rapid when the subject is initially alert, and that the onset of drowsiness may lead to complex changes in physiological responses, especially in the amount of alpha rhythm. The background alpha rhythm is maximal at the level of alert, relaxed attention, and disappears at higher or lower levels of arousal.

Inhibition

Habituation is thought to be due to active inhibition of the neural response (Pavlov, 1927). Mackworth (1950) suggested that the decrement in detections found during a vigilance task was due to internal inhibition, in the sense that the decrease or absence of response was the result of the repeated stimuli incorporated in the task itself. Oldfield (1937) mentioned that internal inhibition was usually due to the regular occurrence of simple, discrete changes. Mackworth considered that the regular jumps of the clock hand satisfied this condition. In further discussion, he pointed out that the absence of reinforcement of the detection responses allowed inhibition to occur. In addition to this, changes in expectancy could account for many of the fluctuations in behaviour occurring during the session. This formulation remains a valid description of the theoretical approach of this book, but recent advances in neurological knowledge allow an elaboration of the concept of inhibition in neurological terms. It is proposed that the failure to respond to a signal arises from habituation of the neural responses to the repeated *background events* of the task, rather than being an extinction of the detection response itself, since the data do not support the direct analogy between experimental extinction and the detection response.

In many ways the actual part played by neural inhibition in habituation and performance is still speculative, but intensive study is being devoted to the subject, and it is hoped that soon there will be general agreement on some of the concepts tentatively outlined in this chapter.

McDaniel and White (1966), in discussing the causes of habituation, mentioned that most recent observers favour the anticipatory theory of habituation, as selective attenuation of the sensory response to insignificant and irrelevant stimuli. They distinguished this view from the *internal inhibition* of Pavlov (1927) which involved learning not to respond. Internal inhibition often expressed itself as brief periods of sleep, occurring when a significant stimulus was not expected. A distinction has already been drawn between habituation of the neural effects of the stimulus, both specific and non-specific, and changes in the over-all level of arousal. It is probable that both these changes are found in a vigilance task. Several authors (e.g., Baker, Ware and Sipowicz, 1962; McGrath, 1960) have mentioned that some of their subjects fell asleep during a session, and the probability that occasional periods of drowsiness may have escaped notice is high, since Oswald (1962) has mentioned that the EEG signs of sleep were often present in monotonous tasks even when the eyes were open. The rest of this chapter will, however, be concerned with inhibition of the neural response to a repetitive stimulus.

Experimental Extinction

Experimental extinction involves the disappearance of a conditioned response when it is not reinforced. Mackworth (1950) suggested that the vigilance decrement was due to experimental extinction, occurring because the response to the signal was not reinforced. He based this suggestion on the facts that knowledge of results maintained the level of performance, and a strong stimulus, namely a telephone message, produced disinhibition. Humphrey (1930) pointed out the similarity of habituation and experimental extinction, and Thompson and Spencer (1966) mentioned that the major parametric relations characteristic of habituation are also characteristic of extinction. Habituation, however, is a term usually applied to unlearned responses, while experimental extinction is by definition related to the extinction of the conditioned response.

Mackworth (1950) considered that the extinguished response was the motor response indicating that a signal had occurred. The recent finding that false alarms also tend to be reduced during the vigilance task agrees with this suggestion. Two difficulties arise, however. The finding that the decrement is greater with *fewer* signals is contrary to the idea of experimental extinction, which is faster when there are more unreinforced responses. Secondly, there is the difficulty that the vigilance decrement reaches a plateau after a while, often at a level only 10–15 per cent below the original level. Mackworth suggested that *expectancy* maintained the level of performance, since after half an hour the subject had a good idea of the mean probability of signals. The recent finding that the level of detection and the rate of decrement depend very strongly on the background event rate has shifted the interest towards the effect of the non-signal events. The response that is being extinguished may be thought of as the neural response to these repetitive non-signal events, while the detection of an occasional signal will act as a reinforcement, and so maintain performance at a level somewhere below the maximum or alert performance. These neural responses to the incoming non-signal events may also be thought of as observing responses, (see Mackworth, 1970), and their inhibition may be mediated by the hippocampus (see p. 102).

Stimulus-produced Inhibition

Eysenck (1963) has considered the various aspects of stimulus-produced inhibition. He pointed out that this concept applied to vigilance, reminiscence, and adaptation (habituation). The basic theory was that the decrement in performance in various repetitive tasks was due not to a failure of reinforcement of the response, but to a repetition or continuation of the stimulus. Since decrements in performance occur even in active tracking tasks, (see chapter 2), it would seem that stimulus-produced inhibition is not dependent on a large number of non-signal events. There does, however, seem to be evidence that the ratio of signal to non-signal events is an important factor in determining the rate and nature of the decrement.

Of particular interest was the suggestion by Eysenck (1963) that inhibitory processes occurred more rapidly in extraverts than in introverts. He suggested that the optimal level of stimulation was much lower for introverts for this reason. They would therefore be expected to be better at tasks, such as vigilance, that offered low levels of stimulation. Extraverts should show greater reminiscence than introverts, since reminiscence is due to the dissipation of stimulus-produced inhibition during a rest pause (see chapter 6).

Eysenck further suggested that stimulant drugs would have an introverting effect, and depressive drugs an extraverting effect. If the relationship discussed in the previous paragraph is true, then this also follows, since these drugs maintain or depress performance in a vigilance task respectively. The effect of alcohol, a depressant, is well known to increase apparent extraversion. Its initial effect is often an increase in activity, especially in conversation, because it removes the social inhibitions that normally interfere with a ready flow of words. In vigilance, it has been shown that a depressant drug may increase false responses, or at least maintain the initial level of false responses, while depressing the correct responses (see chapter 8). Amphetamine, a stimulant drug, increases or maintains the level of correct responses, while false responses are not increased. These findings make it clear that a simple decline in the general level of activation is not an adequate explanation of the vigilance decrement. Since inhibition by definition is an active process, it may be decreased by depressant drugs. If the changes in a vigilance task were merely due to passive reduction of activation processes, then depressant drugs should have the same effect on false alarms as continued performance, namely a decrease, whereas in fact the decrease in false alarms is maximal with a stimulant drug (Loeb *et al.*, 1965).

Habituation may not occur at all when the animal is anaesthetized, and it is considerably reduced during sleep (Johnson and Lubin, 1967; see p. 96). Therefore, habituation is by no means a passive reduction in reactivity, such as might be expected when sleep occurs. While the arousing properties of the stimulus may be reduced as a result of habituation, there is no direct relation between the level of activation and the degree of habituation, especially of the evoked potential (see chapter 3). Therefore, it is necessary to consider the vigilance decrement as due to two processes which are to some extent independent. A reduction in arousal due to habituation of the orienting response may lead to an increase in false alarms and a decrease in correct detections, while a reduction in the potentials evoked by the repetitive events may lead to a decrease in both kinds of positive responses. In the first case there may be inhibition of the reticular activating system, in the second case an inhibition of the specific neural responses to the stimulus. Which of these two processes is dominant probably depends on the nature of the task, especially on the rate of background events.

Owing to the considerable interest aroused by the concept of activation, inhibition as an active process has tended to be overlooked. The feeling perhaps was that the organism was naturally at a low level of activation, and arousal was produced and maintained by a stream of novel, unexpected or significant stimuli. As the stimulus lost these properties, the activating effect simply died away, like a light when the current is cut off. The matter is not, however, so simple. The incoming energy of the stimuli remains unchanged, but the neural response is actively inhibited, perhaps as a result of the formation of a model.

Models

Sokolov (1963) has discussed the concept of a 'neuronal model of the stimulus' in relation to habituation. Such a model records the properties of a repetitive series of stimuli, both spatial and temporal characteristics. The model acts as a selective filter, inhibiting reaction to a stimulus which closely matches it. When the stimulus differs from the model which it is expected to match, the general orienting reaction may still be inhibited if there is only a small difference, even though the afferent system may be able to distinguish this difference. Sokolov considered that the cortex is essential for the formation of the model and the selective blocking of impulses. Thus the reduction of habituation during sleep may be due to the removal of cortical inhibition.

Douglas and Pribram (1966; see also Douglas, 1967, and Pribram, 1967) have developed the model concept in neurological terms. They suggested that there are two main processes; the first, the reinforce-register, registers the experience, and the second, the error-evaluate process, decreases the probability that an event will be experienced. The first process constructs a model, registration or trace of an event, and the second compares a new event with the model and gates out the event from awareness if it resembles the model. The error-evaluate system is active in extinction and habituation, among other kinds of behaviour.

The complex mechanism is based upon two kinds of neural inhibition, collateral and recurrent. *Collateral* inhibition is the inhibition of one nerve by another, while *recurrent* inhibition is the inhibition of a nerve by its own activity. Collateral inhibition acts to accentuate the difference between active and less active sites, so that an incoming impulse becomes more clearly differentiated from the background noise. Recurrent inhibition equalizes the difference, so that an incoming impulse is less clearly differentiated from the background noise. Side-inhibition is set against self-inhibition. Thus these two forms of inhibition are mutually antagonistic.

Pribram considered that the frontotemporal regions inhibit collateral inhibition, allowing the effects of an event to spread and produce the orienting reflex; the increase in arousal increases awareness of the event and so allows it to be registered. Thus one may be reading a book or listening to a talk, but unless attention is being paid to the incoming stimulus, nothing reaches the long-term storage. Pribram, like Sokolov, suggested that this registration system was insensitive to errors, or slight differences between one stimulus and another.

The error-evaluate system is related to the hippocampus. Pribram suggested that this system inhibited recurrent inhibition, allowing an erroneous experience to register as such. Habituation, on the other hand, is due to enhancement of recurrent inhibition. It prevents a repetitive event from reaching awareness.

It was suggested by Bagshaw, Kimble and Pribram (1965; see p. 86) that the orienting reaction is made up of two parts, the alerting reaction and a focusing function which allows registration of the event and is related to GSR. The neural process following a repetitive event may therefore be considered in four stages (Pribram, 1967).

(1) *The alerting reaction*, due to enhancement of collateral inhibition by the specific sensory mechanisms, leads to (2) *Focusing and registration*, due to inhibition of collateral inhibition, mediated by the frontotemporal cortex, and result-

ing in (3) *Enhancement of self-inhibition*, leading to habituation and finally to (4) *Evaluation and registration of errors*, due to inhibition of self-inhibition by the hippocampus.

The first stage involves recognition and identification of the stimulus. The two first stages can be regarded as essential in the formation of a memory trace, or model. It has been suggested by J. F. Mackworth (1963a; 1966) that, in the initial stages of memorizing, attention is divided between identifying the material and storing it. Material which requires more attention to identify is more difficult to recall. It can be seen that the first two stages described above are antagonistic, since the first enhances and the second inhibits collateral inhibition. The first stage must involve recognition, since no orienting reaction occurs if the material is recognized as familiar. In this stage, the specific sensory mechanism is dominant, and it inhibits other processes. In the second stage, there is an activation of secondary or collateral processes, so that the material can be registered, perhaps in the temporal cortex.

The interference resulting from division of attention between two events may be related to the first stage. Each neural response inhibits the other parts of the brain, in order to produce maximum distinction between the active and inactive areas. When two channels are competing for attention, each will exert an inhibiting effect on the other.

As a result of these four possibilities, enhancement and inhibition of collateral and recurrent inhibition, the neural mechanisms are delicately balanced to allow registration of experience and neglect of the familiar. The mechanisms lose their efficiency when the series of events are closely similar to each other, and small changes requiring response are themselves repetitive, even though temporally irregular. It would appear that in such a case the evolutionary necessity for awareness to be kept free for the novel and dangerous event overrides the specific requirement to be alert for the signal events that differ so little from other events in the task.

Sokolov and Pribram emphasize the part played by cortical levels of awareness in model building and habituation. Habituation is, however, a very basic property of polysynaptic neural chains, occurring at all levels from the nerve net of the sea-anemone, and from the spinal to the cortical, in higher animals (Sharpless and Jasper, 1956; Thompson and Spencer, 1966). Therefore, it is not surprising that habituation of neural responses in a repetitive task should override the more recent and delicate error-evaluate system unless awareness is maintained by some other means than the central events of the task (see chapter 9).

Hernández-Peón and Sterman (1966) pointed out that there is a range of structures, beginning with the prefrontal cortex, which when stimulated produce response inhibition; when destroyed, responses are excessive and prolonged. Thus, the reduction of responses in the vigilance situation, both correct and incorrect, might be related to the activation of this system.

Magoun (1963, 1965) discussed neurological inhibition in detail (ibid. 1965, pp. 68–73). The frontal and temporal lobes are particularly important in internal inhibition. Ablation prevents the habituation of the orienting reflex, so that the animal becomes readily distractible, and external inhibition may be increased. The thalamocortical system is also important in internal inhibition. Stimulation of the paramedial thalamic region of the cat produces sleep (Hess, 1944), and also produces widespread recruiting or synchronization of the cortical EEG (Morison and Dempsey, 1942). Monnier et al., (1960) showed that this non-specific thalamocortical system contained both arousing and inhibiting components. The latter produced synchronization of the EEG and fired best at low stimulus frequencies. Other systems, such as the bulbo-pontile brain stem and the hypothalamus, may drive this synchronizing system. Magoun concluded that the thalamocortical mechanism for internal inhibition was antagonistic to the ascending reticular activating system. He pointed out that in every category in which Pavlov has found internal inhibition, hypersynchronization has been found in the EEG.

Summary and Conclusions

Habituation is a decline in innate responses due to repetition of the stimulus. Habituation of the orienting response includes changes that may decrease the sensitivity of the organism to a stimulus as well as its readiness to respond. This decrease in sensitivity results not only from peripheral changes but also from changes in the central nervous system. The spontaneous rhythms increase, so that the incoming signals are less distinguishable from the neural noise.

Several features of habituation of physiological responses have also been found in vigilance tasks. The most important are (1) the exponential decay of the probability of response, whether correct or incorrect, as measured by changes in the two statistics, d′ and beta[2]; (2) the finding that the level and rate of decrement are proportional to the background event rate (see Mackworth, 1970).

While the usual arousal response in the CNS is the appearance of the desynchronized low-amplitude electrical activity often known as beta rhythm, after habituation the neural response may involve the appearance of alpha rhythm. This may coincide with a decrease in reaction time. The alpha response may also occur when a false motor response is given.

In the normal subject, habituation may occur as a result of a cortical process, which constructs a model of the incoming stimuli, and then compares new stimuli with this model. If the new stimulus agrees with the model in all features, including temporal occurrence, then the neural response to the stimulus may be inhibited. The generalized response will be inhibited first, and later the specific cortical response, as well as more peripheral responses.

Habituation may result from an increase in the normal self- or recurrent inhibition by which a nerve damps down its own response. This process may be mediated by the fronto-limbic system, and may be the mechanism for Pavlov's in-

2. d′ is a measure of sensitivity. Beta is a measure of the criterial level. Both are derived from the proportions of hits and false alarms.

ternal inhibition. Eysenck has given it the name of stimulus-produced inhibition, since it results from a repetition of the stimulus. He has suggested that this inhibition occurs more rapidly in extraverts, who are more dependent on the environment for arousal than are introverts.

In any particular situation, the stimuli reaching the organism will initially produce increased arousal and maximal evoked potentials. The orienting response to environmental stimuli will habituate more rapidly than the response to those stimuli about which a discrimination must be made. As the task stimuli are repeated, the orienting response to them will also habituate. As a result of the increased variance of the neural noise, the threshold for stimuli presented against an unchanging or very rapidly changing background may thus be increased. When, however, the task requires discrimination of a difference between members of a series of stimuli, habituation of the evoked potential response to the background events of the task may not necessarily lead to decreased sensitivity for the difference. In fact, a difference between two events may be more easily detected when the absolute intensity of the events is reduced (Weber's Law). There may, however, be a decreased number of events that reach a certain criterial level; hence, both detections and false alarms may be reduced. Moreover, if the arousing property of a stimulus is rewarding, then habituation of this property may increase the cost of making an observing response (see Mackworth, 1970); a reduction in the number of observing responses may also reduce the number of detections and false alarms.

In conclusion, it is suggested that the changes in a vigilance task are related to habituation of the neural responses to the repetitive or continuous *background events* of the task. These neural events include both the arousal response and the evoked potential. The arousal response may either disappear or may change from an alpha block to an alpha burst as the background rhythm changes from alpha to low-amplitude random activity. In either case the high-amplitude alpha may interfere with discrimination of the signal.

6 Vigilance and Arousal, Individual Differences

The definition of *vigilance* suggested by Mackworth (1957) referred to 'the readiness of the subject to detect and respond to a specified small change in the environment', in other words, a particular signal. The *orienting response* creates a state of readiness to detect, identify, and if necessary respond to whatever has produced the state of alertness by a novel or unexpected stimulus. Thus there may be considered to be a fairly close resemblance between these two states. There need not necessarily be any relation between the over-all level of activation and the strength of the orienting response evoked by a particular stimulus. Moreover, the rate of habituation of the orienting response to a repeated stimulus is not necessarily related to the general level of activation of the organism, in so far as there is such a definable state as a general level of activation. Therefore, the question of the relationship between vigilance and activation can be considered under four headings: (1) changes in physiological measures of activation; (2) evidence about the arousal effect of a signal or other experimental variables; (3) indirect evidence about conditions which are assumed to have an arousing effect; and (4) individual differences in vigilance performance and changes in arousal measures. Despite several years of discussion of the theory of arousal in relation to vigilance, there is not very much direct evidence on either of the first two questions.

1. *Physiological measures of arousal during a vigilance task*

Skin conductance has been found to decrease during a vigilance task, especially for those subjects who show a decrease in performance (Andreassi, 1966a and b; Dardano, 1962;

Davies and Krkovic, 1965; Eason, Beardshall and Jaffee, 1965; Ross, Dardano and Hackman, 1959; Stern, 1966). Skin conductance is closely related to overall levels of arousal (Duffy, 1962, p. 59), being lowest during sleep. Stern (1964) showed that when subjects were required to indicate auto-kinetic movements of a light, there was a decrease in skin conductance during the session. Subjects in the same situation who had no task to do showed a greater decrease in skin conductance. Thus, although the monotony of the situation produced a decrease in arousal in both groups, the requirement of making a decision helped to maintain the level of arousal.

With *reaction time experiments* there were significant correlations between increase in R T and decrease in skin conductance during a session, and also between over-all levels of R T and skin conductance (see p. 123). Freeman (1940) found that as skin conductance decreased, R T increased except at very high levels of skin conductance. With *detection* experiments, however, although skin conductance decreases during the task, significant correlations between trends in detections and skin conductance have not been demonstrated.

The rate of *spontaneous G S R* decreases when the proba-bility of detecting a signal is low (Surwillo and Quilter, 1965).

The E E G spontaneous or background activity may show changes characteristic of sleep after a few minutes spent on a monotonous auditory task. When signals occur during such episodes there may be no response (Oswald, 1962). D. R. Davies and Krkovic (1965) found decreases in *z*-scores for alpha rhythm and detections during an auditory vigilance task that were closely parallel to each other.

The measure of the amount of alpha rhythm may bear a U-shaped relation to the arousal level. The alpha rhythm only appears as a background rhythm at a particular level of arousal, and above or below this level it is absent. Thus, a decrease in alpha may represent either a decrease in alertness, as above, and as Morell (1966) found (see p. 95), or an increase. Thorsheim (1967) measured integrated alpha rhythm before and after a six-second signal in a vigilance task. The signal was a change from the number 30 to the number 70.

There were five signals in each ten minutes. During the longest interval the experimental subjects went through a series of exercises. There was significantly less alpha immediately after exercise than in the same period with the control group. This was taken as indicating that the exercise increased the level of arousal. The control subjects showed greater arousal (less alpha) after the signal than before. There was, however, no significant relationship between the increase in reaction time during the session and the changes in alpha. McFarland *et al.* (1942) found that exercise improved the visual sensitivity of subjects who had been tested for half an hour. Thorsheim suggested that perhaps arousal affects visual sensitivity but not motor systems. The work of Lansing, Schwartz and Lindsley (1959) however, showed a direct relation between speed of reaction and the amount of alpha block. Morell (1966) also found that when the EEG pattern changed to a desynchronized background pattern, with bursts of alpha occurring after a signal, the reaction time was longer than when the alpha rhythm constituted the background activity.

The relation between the EEG and performance in an auditory digit task was examined by Daniel (1967). The intersignal variability was increased with successive time blocks. There was an increase in the amount of alpha concurrently with an increase in omissions and reaction times. There was, however, no direct relation between omissions and the amount of alpha. This might be expected, since alpha may disappear with either an increase or a decrease in arousal. An unexpected finding was that there was a decrease in theta waves just before an omission. These waves are usually considered to be a sign of drowsiness. Daniel pointed out that hippocampal theta might be a correlate of attentional behaviour.

Wilkinson, Morlock and Williams (1966) recorded evoked potentials during an auditory vigilance task (see Figure 15a, b and c) and found that there was a correlation between the increased amplitude of the late negative wave and missed signals. This change they considered to be characteristic of a decrease in arousal. Wilkinson and Morlock (1967), however, found no correlation between any components of the auditory evoked response and reaction time.

2. The effect of experimental conditions on activation measures

Signal rate. Eason *et al.* (1965) examined the effect of signal rate on skin conductance. There was a tendency for there to be a higher percentage of detections and higher skin conductance with the slow signal rate, but the differences between the rates were not significant. Usually the tendency is towards a lower percentage of detections with a slower signal rate (see Mackworth, 1970). Stern (1966) examined the detection of small movements of a point of light. He also found a more rapid decrease in skin conductance with a faster signal rate, but a lower percentage of signals was detected with slower signal rate. There was a marked increase in false alarms during the session with the slow signal rate, together with a decrease in correct detections. Stern suggested that this increase in false alarms was due to autokinetic movements of the light.

Noise. Intermittent fluctuating noise had no effect on either reaction time or skin conductance in a vigilance task (Dardano, 1962).

Knowledge of results. Coules and Avery (1966) found that KR did not affect conductance levels but did decrease RT for males. For females, RT was not decreased by KR but conductance was increased.

3. Indirect evidence about conditions which are assumed to have an effect on the level of arousal

This topic will be dealt with in chapters 7 and 8 (see also Mackworth, 1970). One example may be discussed here. Catalano (1967) and Catalano and Whalen (1967a and b) investigated the hypothesis that the decrement in the rotary pursuit task might be due to habituation of the arousal response. They found that the improvement between trials (reminiscence) was increased when subjects spent the interval squeezing a dynamometer or turning a disc against resistance.

4. *Individual differences in performance and arousal measures*

It has proved difficult to obtain reliable correlations between performance in a vigilance task and changes in any particular measure of arousal. Moreover, correlation between performance in two kinds of vigilance task has also proved low in many cases. These difficulties may be due to the fact that there is no such thing as a characteristic state of arousal or vigilance or to the presence of a number of different factors that influence performance and changes in the various measures of arousal.

A. Individual Differences in Vigilance Tasks

Large differences between subjects are consistently found in vigilance tasks. This has led to the hope that selection tests could be devised for monitoring tasks. Results however, suggest that the best selection test for a particular vigilance task is that task itself. In any particular vigilance task, individuals may differ in a number of ways. They may differ in their ability to detect the signal under alerted conditions, or in their basic reaction time. Secondly, they may differ in the rate at which their performance deteriorates during the task. Thirdly, they may differ in their criterial level, the level of probability at which they are prepared to respond. This criterion may depend on the whole past history of the subject, as well as on his estimates of the requirements of the particular task. In particular, the rate at which signals were given in training will affect the criterion (Colquhoun and Baddeley, 1964, 1967). Fourthly, subjects may differ in the level of activity or arousal according to their own past history, including such environmental variables as the time of day, hours of sleep, coffee and so on. Any investigation of individual differences should, if possible, take all these considerations into account. Clearly this is not possible, nor is it possible to transfer findings in a laboratory situation to performance in a standard job such as inspection without an investigation of performance in the job itself, unknown to the subject. Motivation is a very powerful factor in performance.

The relationship between performance in an alerted version of the task and over-all level of performance in the main task is probably the most reliable finding. Comparisons of decrement rates at different levels of over-all performance are considerably less reliable.

Relation between initial level and rate of decrement

It is very difficult to compare the rate of decrement at two different levels. Changes in percentage of detections should have quite different weightings in different percentile ranges. More reliable comparisons can be made with measures for sensitivity (d') and criterion (beta), when these are available. McGrath (1965) presented data from which calculations of d' and beta could be made. When detections changed from 96 to 87 per cent, d' declined from 4·5 to 4·0; with a more difficult signal, detections declined from 75 to 42 per cent, but d' only fell from 2·3 to 1·9. When the signal is nearer to the threshold, very small changes in sensitivity will make large changes in detections.

Mackworth (1950) divided his subjects into good and bad on the basis of their initial level of detections. Those who detected 92 per cent in the first half-hour detected 87 per cent in the next three half-hours. Poor subjects detected 70 per cent initially and less than 50 per cent in the final half-hour. These figures are very similar to those reported above, obtained when the difficulty of the signal was varied.

McGrath (1960) found that trained sonarmen performed only a little better than casual naval personnel in the pre-test, but showed considerably less decrement during the vigilance session. The difference in performance was maintained in the post-test, indicating that the trained men had improved in their ability to detect the signal. Thus, the difference between the two groups might have been due to the fact that the trained men were learning during the session.

Relation between performance at different times during the task

Jenkins (1958) found high correlations between two sessions on the meter deflection task, indicating that subjects were consistent in their ability to detect signals on this task. Buckner, Harabedian and McGrath (1960; see Buckner, 1963, p. 171–9) found that individual differences were highly consistent between pre-test and main watch, and were stable over long periods of time in a particular task, but showed a low correlation between sensory modes. Those subjects who detected fewest signals in the alerted pre-test showed a greater decrement during the session, with the visual task. With an auditory task the difference in decrement between good and poor subjects was not significant.

Relation between performance on two or more tasks

Baker (1963b) compared performance on two kinds of visual vigilance tasks, the continuous clock test and the dial test, and concluded that there was not a vigilance factor, since correlations between the two tasks were low. It would seem very likely that more than one factor is important when comparing two kinds of vigilance tasks, but it cannot as yet be concluded that one of the relevant factors is not a change in a generalized readiness to detect and respond, though this state is hard to separate from other relevant factors. Baker found that there were significant correlations between performance on successive days, but with the dial test, performance on the first day did not correlate significantly with performance on later days. The continuous clock has been found to be somewhat unusual among vigilance tasks, since a consistent decline in sensitivity (d') has been found during a session (Mackworth and Taylor, 1963). Baker found that with both tasks, there was high correlation between performance on successive hours of the task.

Cross-modality comparisons have been made by a number of authors. Buckner, Harabedian and McGrath (1965) found high correlations between pre-test and main watch, between successive periods of a watch and between watches within a mode, but correlations between performance on visual and auditory tasks were low. It was found, however, that subjects who were in the upper half of the group for performance on the visual task were also in the upper half of the group in the auditory task.

Eijkman and Vendrick (1965) compared fluctuations in sensitivity for auditory and visual signals. The signals were changes in either the intensity or the duration of events. There was no significant correlation between detections of intensity changes, but detections of duration were highly correlated. Gunn and Loeb (1967) also examined sensitivity to changes in intensity in visual and auditory pulses. There were significant correlations for sensitivity (d′) in all sessions. There were also significant correlations in the criterial level (beta) in the first session, but not in the second session. Hatfield and Loeb (1968) compared an auditory task, a closely coupled visual task with the eyes closed, and a loosely coupled visual task. Nearly all correlations between hits in the different tasks were significant, but there were no significant correlations between false alarms in the visual and auditory modes. The two visual tasks showed high correlations for d′, beta and latencies, but only one of the four comparisons between the visual and auditory modes showed significant correlations for d′ and beta. All correlations were, however, positive. The data suggested that changes in false alarms were not due entirely to the same factor that caused the reductions in detections.

R. A. Baker and Ware (1966) tested subjects on four different monotonous tasks. These were a simple vigilance task, a bean-sorting task, a simple assembly task and a two-digit addition task. There was a decrement during the session with the first two tasks, and an improvement with the other two. No significant correlations were found between vigilance performance and the other tasks.

B. Relation Between Various Test Scores and Vigilance
Performance and Attempts to Predict Ability

It would seem that if reliable correlations between tasks are so
diffcult to obtain, then it would be useless to seek for tests
which will predict performance on a vigilance task. The situation is not, however, as bad as this. When a careful examination is made of the relevant factors, it has been found that
there may be a relation between temperament and performance
on a monotonous or repetitive task. Eysenck (1963) suggested
that introverts should show more stable performance in a
monotonous task than extraverts (see p. 99). Other names
for these types are inner-directed and outer-directed; when
neurotic, introverts become dysthymic or obsessional, while
extraverts become hysteric. Jung (1923) has pointed out that
for the extravert, 'interest and attention follow objective
happenings, and, primarily, those of the immediate environment'. It would therefore follow that the extravert should be
most sensitive to novelty, and therefore the repetitive stimulus
should most rapidly lose its stimulating effect on him. The
introvert, on the other hand, 'interposes a subjective view
between the perception of the object and his own action'
(Jung, ibid, 1959 edn, p. 216). Thus the introvert will be more
affected by his motivation, by his desire to do the task well,
than by the habituating effects of the stimulus.

Broadbent (1958) reported a number of experiments in
which extraverts, diagnosed in various ways, were shown to
perform poorly on prolonged tasks as compared with introverts. Such task as the twenty-lights test, the twenty-dials
test and the five-choice serial reaction task all showed that
extraverts tended to have a higher rate of decrement in the
session than introverts. It was also found that introverts
showed a greater tendency to continue with prolonged
training and to do better in examinations, even though their
intelligence was not different from the other subjects. In these
experiments the index of introversion was 'the triple tester
index', based on the difference between a subject's estimate of
his forthcoming performance on a manual tracking task and

his actual achievement. In other experiments, the index of introversion was the Maudsley questionnaire (Heron, 1956), which was used in many of the following experiments.

Bakan (1959) tested subjects on the digit test, in which digits were repeated at a rate of one per second, and subjects were required to detect three successive odd digits. In one condition there was a secondary task, the detection of all sizes. This secondary task improved performance on the main task. Such an activating effect may be expected, since the secondary task did not distract attention away from the digits to which the subjects were listening. With the two tasks, the extraverts showed much greater decrement than the introverts after the first half hour. With the single task, the extraverts showed very poor initial performance, but by the end of the task the two groups were performing at about the same level.

Another experiment with the same primary task was reported by Bakan, Belton and Toth (1963). Here the introverts detected fewer signals initially than extraverts, but showed an improvement between the first and second periods, so that by the third period they were detecting definitely more signals than the normal or extravert subjects. The two latter groups showed the usual decrement, but the introverts did not. Colquhoun (1960) found that introverts performed better in the morning and extraverts in the afternoon, but he gave no data on changes during the sessions. (See also Bakan, 1963b.)

Tarrière and Hartemann (1964) studied the relationships between smoking, personality and detection (see chapter 8). Figure 34 shows that better performance was found with the introverts and with smoking, and these variables appeared to be additive. All the experiments were carried out in the afternoon. Since the authors found that smokers who were deprived of smoking performed poorly, this variable should be carefully controlled in vigilance experiments. Corcoran (1965) showed that introverts were better than extraverts at the five-choice task, especially with low motivation. The extraverts showed the greatest effect of higher motivating conditions. He also found that with the triple tester, an active tracking task, the extraverts showed a decline with sleep deprivation, while the introverts showed an improvement. He suggested that these data could be interpreted on the assumption that the introverts were hyper-aroused with the active task, while the extraverts were still below their optimal level of arousal. These data he interpreted as supporting the U-shaped curve relating arousal to performance.

Davies and Hockey (1966) also examined the relationship between temperament and performance, in a task in which signal frequency and the noise level were varied. The task involved checking a visual series of digits against a typescript for discrepancies. Signal rates of six or twelve signals in each 8-minute period were given. The noise level was 95 or 70 dB. Extraverts showed a significant decrement in detections in the quiet conditions while introverts showed no decrement in detection in any conditions. A decrease in false alarms was found during each session. The crierial measure (beta) showed an increase in every session (see Mackworth, 1970). This can be interpreted as indicating that the subjects became less ready to give a positive response. The data showed that the criterion of the introverts became most strict at the end of the noise sessions, while the criterion of the extraverts became most strict at the end of the quiet sessions. The sensitivity of the extraverts, as measured by d' (see Mackworth, 1970) showed a decrease during the quiet sessions, while the introverts showed an increase in sensitivity during most sessions, especially with noise (personal communication, Davies and Hockey). The authors interpreted the data in terms of the inverted U-shaped relation between arousal level and performance on the basis that the extraverts detected more signals than the introverts in noise. The fact that the sensitivity of the introverts was higher than that of the extraverts at the end of the noise sessions does not agree with this interpretation. The data do support the suggestion by Eysenck that extraverts are more likely to show inhibition during a repetitive task. It should be noted that subjects were tested in the morning, when introverts have been found to perform better than extraverts at a monotonous task (Colquhoun, 1960; Colquhoun and Corcoran, 1964).

It would therefore seem that on the whole introverts do perform better than extraverts on a vigilance task. This can perhaps be linked with other dimensions of personality, such as the stabile–labile scale, and possibly with the excitability scale (Duffy, 1962; Lacey, 1967; see p. 128).

Other tests

Other tests, especially those testing attitude or temperament, have also shown significant relationships with performance in a vigilance task. Halcomb and Kirk (1965) extracted certain factors from a battery of tests. Reaction time was significantly shorter with those subjects who rated high on 'flexibility' but there was no differential effect of this factor on time periods. On the other hand, there were significant interactions between time periods and the level of the factor of 'self-control'. Of particular interest was the factor of 'achievement via independence' (A I). This showed significant triple interaction with intelligence and time periods. Subjects who had high intelligence levels and high A I showed short reaction times throughout the four hours of the test. Subjects with medium levels of A I began at the same level as the previous group but showed a considerable increase in reaction times during the session. Subjects with low A I showed long reaction times throughout the task. This experiment seems to be a very promising one for disentangling some of the variables that differentiate subjects. It would be very interesting to know how these factors relate to the introversion factor. Self-control and A I might well be related to inner-directedness.

Intelligence

There seems to be little relationship between vigilance performance and intelligence as a factor by itself. Ware (1961) studied a range of 50 to 143 I Q on the G T (verbal and and arithmetic reasoning) test. There was no relation between intelligence and signal detection on either visual or auditory tasks. Ware, Baker and Sipowicz (1962) tested a group of mental deficients, with a mean I Q of 58. These were compared with a group of normal subjects and it was found that there was no significant difference in detection. They found, however, that when knowledge of results was added to the task, by flashing a light when the subjects had missed a signal, this produced an initial improvement but did not maintain the performance of the defectives. Thus it appeared that the defectives could do the task, but could not benefit so well from non-verbal instructions about their performance. (See also Sipowicz and Baker, 1961.)

Jerison (1965) tested monkeys in a vigilance task, and found that they could perform well, even better than humans; when the intensity of shock reinforcement was raised, they stopped facing the signal source, but responded very frequently. By penalizing false alarms, the strategy could be returned to the correct pattern of behaviour. Polidora and Urbanek (1964) also examined the ability of monkeys to detect signals, which were special patterns of lights. False responses increased with pentobarbital and small doses of chlorpromazine, but decreased with large doses of chlorpromazine. With a small dose of chlorpromazine, detection of difficult signals was greatly decreased, though detection of easy signals was not affected until a large dose was given. J. C. Wilson (1965) found a similar result (see also Delorge et al., 1967). Work on the detection of signals by rats, and the effect of drugs, has been reported by Kornetsky and Bain (1965) and Uehling and Venator (1967).

McGrath (1963b) correlated thirty-five different tests with performance in a vigilance task and found no consistently significant relationships. This might be because there are a number of interacting factors. If performance depends to some extent on the relative values of observing or not observing the display, it is clear that a number of factors will affect these values for the subject. In most experiments the only reward lies in the satisfaction of detecting a signal. Bakan (1963a) related answers to a questionnaire and detections. He found that subjects who regarded the task as interesting and challenging detected more signals than subjects who were bored or distracted. He identified this as an arousal factor.

Subjects were able to evaluate their performance fairly well. They recognized that they had missed some signals, indicating that they were adopting a strict criterion.

McGrath and Harabedian (1963) asked their subjects to estimate how many signals they thought had occurred in a watch. Subjects who thought there had been only a few signals had actually detected more signals than subjects who estimated that there had been many. This difference was particularly marked for those signals following a long interval. The first group detected most signals in this category, while the second group detected fewest, although these differences were not significant. Since most subjects gave no false alarms, they were clearly employing a very strict criterion. Therefore, the difference between their estimates and their performance must have been due to those observations about which they were doubtful. If one group used a stricter criterion than the other, this strict group would respond less often, but perhaps made allowance for their criterion in making their estimate of the actual number of signals. In other words, they thought that they had missed a lot of signals. That subjects do have a considerable category of doubtful signals has been demonstrated by Broadbent and Gregory (1965).

C. Individual Differences in Measures of Arousal

In addition to the fact that performance on two kinds of vigilance task do not correlate highly with each other, it has been found that different measures of arousal do not necessarily correlate highly with each other either. Lacey (1967) has pointed out that there are different kinds of arousal, autonomic, electrocortical and behavioural. He has emphasized that individuals show idiosyncratic patterns of autonomic responding, and that the direction rather than the degree of change is the important finding for activation. Thus, the most that can be hoped for in relating performance changes to autonomic or E E G changes is that one particular physiological measure will show a monotonic relationship to performance.

Attempts have been made to characterize subjects by the number of spontaneous autonomic responses that they produce independently of external stimuli. In particular, the GSR appears to be a promising measure in predicting changes during a task. Subjects who show many of these responses when resting are defined as labile, while those showing few resting responses are defined as stabiles. Mundy-Castle and McKiever (1953) found that stabiles showed greater adaptation (habituation) of GSR to repetitive auditory stimulation. Johnson (1963) measured spontaneous GSR at rest and in the intervals between presenting a tone or a burst of flickering light. He found that the stabile subjects showed rapid adaptation, in the sense that the number of spontaneous GSR between stimuli were reduced with repetition of the stimuli. The labile subjects showed much less habituation. Heart rate responses did not habituate with either group. He found that there was no correlation with other measures such as EEG amplitude or alpha index, or heart rate. He concluded that significant correlations are more likely to be found when the subjects are either in a state of high or low arousal, but not when they are in the intermediate state of relaxed wakefulness.

Koepke and Pribram (1966) examined spontaneous GSR in relation to tones presented at random intervals. Labiles showed much slower habituation than stabiles, in the sense that they took longer to reach a criterion of three successive failures to respond by GSR to a tone. On the other hand, the labiles reached an asymptote sooner than the stabiles, who were still showing habituation at the end of thirty-three trials. It was found that labiles gave faster overt responses to the tones. The authors found a weak negative relation between spontaneous activity and base conductance level (see Figure 19).

D. Relation between Individual Levels of Performance and Physiological Measures

Surwillo and Quilter (1965) examined the performance of

subjects on the clock test. They tested two groups, subjects under sixty years of age and subjects from sixty to eighty-five. They found that the older subjects showed a greater decrement in detection and fewer spontaneous GSR. They also found that there were significantly fewer spontaneous GSR in the eighteen seconds before a signal was missed than in a similar interval before a signal was detected. This relationship was

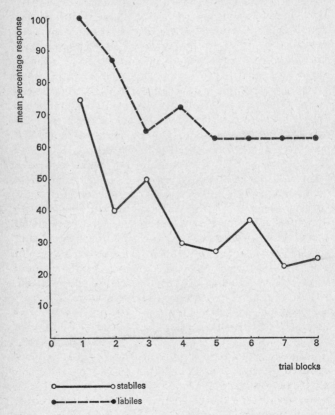

Figure 19 Mean percentage GSR to pure tones given at random intervals to human subjects (from Koepke and Pribram, 1966, p. 445)

not due to a common trend over time, because it was found even with those subjects who missed more signals in the early part of the test. There was, however, a decrease in spontaneous GSR during the session. They also found that labiles showed a shorter reaction time than did stabiles.

Basal skin conductance

Dardano (1962) examined the relationship between basal skin conductance and reaction time in a visual vigilance task. Speed of reaction and conductance both showed decrements during the session. Subjects could, however, be divided into those who showed significant correlations between reaction time and conductance and those who did not. The first group showed a continuous fall in conductance and a marked rise in reaction time diring the session, while the second group showed an initial rise in conductance and only a small increase in reaction time during the session. It therefore appeared that those subjects who regarded the task as a challenge maintained their performance level better than subjects who adopted a more relaxed attitude.

Andreassi (1966a) presented a 200 cycle-per-second tone at irregular intervals against a background of white noise. He found that skin conductance decreased and reaction time increased over successive trials. There were thirty-two trials in 40 minutes. Subjects who showed the greatest decrease in conductance showed the greatest percentage increase in reaction times. The highest values of palmar skin conductance were correlated with the shortest reaction times, but the reaction times for the medium and lowest conductance values were not different. Andreassi argued that the U-shaped relation between physiological measures of arousal and performance may be found only when high levels of arousal are obtained by physical work or task-induced stress. A similar suggestion was made by Sherwood (1965). Andreassi (1966b) tested one subject with two patterns of signals. With an irregular pattern (intersignal intervals 10–135 seconds), there was a greater variability of palmar skin conductance values, and a slower reaction time than with a regular signal distribution.

Coules and Avery (1966) also examined changes in basal skin conductance during a vigilance task. The performance measure was the reaction time to a small square of light, appearing at an average rate of once a minute. Knowledge of results was given in one condition. No trends in reaction time were found. The females were slower than the males, and their performance was not improved by knowledge of results. The males showed the fastest reaction time with knowledge of results. Basal skin conductance was lowest for the females with knowledge of results, while the males showed high levels for both conditions, with an increase during the session. Thus there was an over-all relation between basal conductance and reaction time for each sex, but the effect of knowledge of results upon performance was not related to an equivalent change in skin conductance.

Multiple physiological measures

McNulty and Noseworthy (1966) have discussed and investigated the varying patterns of activation in relation to performance on the pursuit rotor and finger dexterity test. Subjects were classified on the basis of their most active physiological index. Measures were taken of blood pressure, heart rate, electromyographic potential (EMG) and skin resistance. The most active index was that one which was highest above the group mean for a particular subject.

Subjects who were to perform under conditions of high arousal were given a shock just before the task and told that they would receive another shock if their performance was below the norm. It was found that those subjects whose most active index was skin resistance showed about the same level of performance under conditions of high and low arousal while the other subjects performed better under high arousal on both the tests. The group whose most active index was blood pressure showed the best performance when tested under high arousal. It has been suggested that changes in blood pressure may be the physiological factor that acts directly on the reticular system (Baust and Niemczyk, 1964). Thus it is possible that these subjects had the highest level of arousal. On the other hand, it is possible that these subjects were extraverts who would be most sensitive to external events such as shock.

Eason, Beardshall and Jaffee (1965) examined several physiological indices of performance during a visual vigilance task with two signal rates, 120 or thirty per hour. They found that none of the dependent variables was affected significantly by the signal rate. There was a significant decrement in detections and in skin conductance during the session, an increase in neck EMG and no significant change in heart rate and vertical eye movements. There was, however, a significant correlation between performance decrement and changes in vertical eye movements during the session. The latter tended to increase as the session continued. Correlations between changes in the other variables were not significant. With regard to the signal rates, there was a significant correlation between the ratios of performance scores and skin conductance on the two rates. Conductance was lower with the fast signal rate. False reports were extremely few, but slightly more for the slow signal rate. There was a tendency for heart rate, skin conductance and EMG scores to correlate positively, but not the vertical eye movements. There was, therefore, very little evidence that the changes in performance during the session were due to changes in arousal. Although the skin conductance measures fell, this fall was not correlated with changes in performance. In this task, the event rate was twenty per minute. With these slow event rates, the decrement in detection is probably related to habituation of the evoked potential rather than to changes in arousal. The authors suggested that subjects were more highly activated during the slow signal rate.

Stern (1966) examined the relationship between detection of a movement of a point of light and changes in various physiological indices. There were two signal rates, 120 or sixty per hour. He found that there was a decrement in detections and a marked increase in false alarms during the session with the slow signal rate. This suggests that there was a decrement in d′ during the session with the slow signal rate. There might also have been a slight decrement in d′ with the fast signal rate, which showed a decrement in detections and a very slight increase in false alarms during the session. These results support the suggestion (see Mackworth, 1968; 1970) that decrements in d′ may be a result of continuous or very fast background event rates, since in this experiment the point of light was unmoving except when a signal occurred. There was a considerable increase in skin resistance during the session, and this increase was greater with the faster signal rate. This is the same result as that found by Eason *et al.* (1965).

Stern found that there was an increased variability of EMG activity of the neck with the slow signal rate and a slight decrease with the fast signal rate, as compared with the pre-task level. The author suggested that the group receiving the slow signal rate was overly aroused and responded to irrelevant stimuli. Measures of heart rate and respiration rate were not related to performance. In view of the fact that both groups showed an increase in skin resistance during the task, the results do not seem consistent with a theory of over-arousal, but the subjects with the low signal rate seem to have made many more responses than the subjects with the fast signal rate, and this high response rate could be expected to maintain arousal. Stern suggested that the false responses were probably examples of the autokinetic phenomenon. An increase in false responses is consistent with a decrease in arousal, since there is an increase in the variability of the background neural patterns with decreased arousal. Depressant drugs can lead to an increase in false alarms (see chapter 8).

These data can be considered under the assumption that when the background event rate of a task is continuous or very fast, changes in evoked potential are not the important factor, but changes in background neural patterns indicating levels of arousal probably are crucial. While reductions in the evoked potential may lead to a reduction in false alarms during the session, changes in arousal patterns, resulting in increasing neural noise, may have the opposite effect. Changes in arousal may also be concomitant with increases in evoked potential.

Adrenalin and performance

O'Hanlon (1964) studied the relationship between performance in a vigilance task and changes in circulating adrenalin and noradrenalin in a vigilance task. A curve relating signal brightness to detection probability was obtained for each subject in a preliminary psychophysical test. Each subject was then tested in the main experiment with that signal level representing 0·9 probability of detection. From this first session of an hour, subjects were divided into two groups depending on whether they showed a significant reduction in detection between pre-test and main watch or not. Three subjects (N group) did not show a decrement. In the final post-test these subjects detected all the signals. The thirteen subjects who did show a decrement (D group) between pre-test and main watch detected about 15 per cent fewer signals in the pre-test than did the N group. It therefore seemed that the experiment was not entirely successful in equating signal detectability in the pre-test. Adrenalin measurements were made while six of the D group were monitoring the vigilance task and seven were watching a movie.

N subjects showed very low levels of adrenalin in the pre-test. Two of the three showed an increase during the vigilance test. The third showed very low levels throughout. For the D group, levels were high in the pre-test and fell during the session. There was a correlation of $r = 0·84$ between adrenalin level and detection. Levels of adrenalin for the control group were low throughout.

These results agree with the suggestion by Buckner (1963) that arousal is greater in a pre-test for those subjects who find the signals more difficult to detect, but that it will rapidly dissipate. There is also the finding that those subjects who find the signal easy to detect show an increase in arousal, as measured by adrenalin, in the main test. Since the N group detected nearly twice as many signals as the D group in the final 2 hours of the test, it might be expected that they could be more aroused if detection itself has an arousing effect.

Subjective impressions

Bakan (1963a) required subjects to answer a seventy-eight-item questionnaire after completing a vigilance task. He found that 94 per cent of the subjects felt drowsy at times; 84 per cent reported involuntary lapses of attention; 77 per cent reported a strong temptation to go to sleep; 75 per cent used physical movements to keep themselves awake; and 86 per cent reported that the detection of a signal made them feel good, indicating that the detection of a signal is rewarding. Twenty-eight of the items showed a significant relationship with detection of signals. These were analysed into five factor loadings. The first factor was identified as arousal or interest, the second and third as evaluation of performance, the fourth as feelings of frustration, and the fifth as motivation. Subjects who admitted that they did not try as hard as they might have done, did poorly on the task. The majority of the subjects were well motivated, 81 per cent said that they expected the task to last longer than it did. This may be compared with the finding by Mackworth (1950) that the subjects were surprised when the 2 hours had elapsed, and thought that there was still some time to go. Time may seem to pass very fast when one is drowsy. Only 42 per cent reported that they tried to figure out when the next signal would arrive, and only 11 per cent reported that they figured out a system of times to listen carefully. Therefore, expectancy did not seem to be an important factor.

Discussion

Gray (1967) has linked the introversion-extraversion scale to two Russian scales of the nervous system. One is the 'weak–strong' scale put forward by Teplov and his fellow workers (see Teplov, 1964). The other is the scale of 'excitation–inhibition' (see Nebylitsyn, 1966). The paper by Gray should be consulted for details of this very interesting discussion. The introvert shares with the weak and the excitatory ends of the scales lower sensory thresholds, a high susceptibility to stimulant drugs such as caffeine, and a higher general level of arousal than subjects at the other ends of the scales. Subjects with a predominance of excitation give prolonged alpha-block responses, which habituate slowly. Sensory thresholds are raised in the weak system by distracting stimuli but lowered in the strong system. Claridge (1960) and Corcoran (1965) found a similar effect of distracting stimuli on introverts and extraverts. Gray also discussed a discrepancy with regard to fatigue of the weak nervous system, and quoted a recent experiment by Rozhdestvenskaya and Yermolayeva-Tomina (1966) showing that individuals with a strong nervous system showed greater physiological signs of fatigue in a vigilance-like situation. The strong nervous system is more stable, thus perhaps, being equivalent to the stabiles (p. 122) who show more rapid habituation.

Gray suggested that all the data could be explained by Eysenck's theory that introverts are chronically more highly aroused than extraverts. As a result, the performance of an introvert may be harmed by too stimulating a situation, while the performance of an extravert will suffer from too little environmental stimulation. The concept of a U-shaped relationship between the level of arousal and performance may be considered in terms of two intersecting processes. It may be postulated that the relation of arousal and sensitivity reaches a maximum at the level where some of the systems are as highly tuned as they can be. For instance, once the EEG rhythm has been reduced to minimum amplitude and maximum frequency, no further change can increase its sensitivity. On the other hand, many of the physiological changes may increase beyond the point at which they improve efficiency, and now they become distracting and interfering. Such changes as too much muscular tension, too great a muscular tremor, too rapid or strong heart beat, and too fast breathing are all familiar to the examinee, who finds these responses to the threatening situation of an oral examination extremely distracting. In such a case, a mild sedative, such as a little alcohol, may actually improve performance by calming 'the nerves' and allowing concentration upon the important aspects of the task. Clearly such an expedient requires careful dosage. Revolver pistol shooting teams working at the Olympic level have been known to switch back to a shot of Scotch after finding that tranquilizers made them slap-happy. The introvert may do better at written examinations, but the extravert may do better at orals, or in highly competitive situations, because for him the added tension is beneficial.

Witkin *et al.* (1962) have suggested that individuals can be classified on the basis of *field-dependency*. Field-dependent people find it difficult to overcome the influence of the field or background; they have difficulty in separating the item from its context. They enjoy contact with others, and show a labile GSR (responsiveness). These people would seem to resemble the extravert type, except for the GSR responsiveness. Field-independent people can align a rod to the true upright, regardless of a tilted frame. They tend to be isolated, over-controlled and distant. This type would seem to correspond with the introvert. An examination of the vigilance performance of such types would be of great interest.

Summary

In conclusion, it would seem that there is evidence that indices of arousal change during a vigilance task. Indeed, it would be surprising if they did not, as the subject sits quietly in a dim room by himself, with a monotonous display in front of him. There is also subjective evidence that subjects are drowsy during the task. It cannot, however, be said that there is convincing evidence that changes in performance during a vigilance task are dependent upon changes in arousal. There is some evidence that certain temperamental factors are important in the changes in performance found in a vigilance task. The introverted subject is affected more by his own thoughts and attitudes than the extravert, who is more dependent on the environmental stimulation. The introvert may show less decrement during a monotonous task than the extravert, and may also be more stable in his physiological responses to a repetitive stimulus. It has been suggested that introverts have lower thresholds and are more aroused. It has also been suggested that subjects who find the task more difficult are more aroused. These two suggestions would appear to cancel each other in effect, since the introverts should be more aroused by temperament, but less aroused because they find the task easier. Percentage changes in detection may be greater when the initial level is lower, though this may represent a change in sensitivity that is equivalent to that at a higher level. It is clear that a great deal of work is required to disentangle all these factors. In particular, detailed studies of changes in physiological measures, at the moment when a signal is seen or missed, are required. It must be remembered, however, that changes in evoked potentials may proceed independently of changes in arousal.

7 Sleep Loss, Noise and Sensory Deprivation

Sleep Loss

Wilkinson (1968) pointed out that a task designed to show the effect of sleep loss must be long, familiar and uninteresting yet complex. The uninteresting yet complex task is one which presents a monotonous and repetitive stimulus, yet there is a high level of uncertainty involved in the decision that is being measured. A vigilance task fulfils all these requirements, provided that the subjects are well practiced at it. In addition, the subjects must be allowed to become familiar with the sleep-deprivation conditions, so that the novelty and challenge is reduced to a minimum. In order to demonstrate the effects of loss of sleep, it is necessary to employ a task which requires continuous attention for at least 15 minutes. There is an interaction between the two stresses of sleep loss and repetitive stimulation, so that the decrement is increased by loss of sleep. Tasks which have been shown to suffer from loss of sleep include:

(a) Self-paced tasks; for example, letter or colour naming, addition sums and the five-choice serial reaction task; (b) Machine-paced tasks of the same kind; and (c) Vigilance tasks.

(a) Self-paced tasks

In tasks in which the subject can proceed at his own pace, the most sensitive measure is the number of blocks, or long reaction times, also known as gaps (see chapter 2). This measure is found to increase more rapidly during the task when the subject is short of sleep (Kleitmann, 1939; 1923; Patrick and Gilbert, 1896; Warren and Clarke, 1937). Bjerner (1949) found that blocks were associated with periods of alpha depression. Armington and Mitnick (1959) found that after fifty hours of sleep deprivation, the alpha rhythm was almost absent, under conditions which in the normal subjects produced maximum alpha, namely with the eyes closed and the mind either blank or counting. Even when mental arithmetic was carried out with the eyes closed, alpha rhythm still tended to disappear after sleep loss, though it was present in the control subjects.

Addition. Wilkinson (1962) presented subjects with a sheet of 100 sums which they were asked to solve as fast as possible for 20 minutes. In the last 5 minutes, knowledge of results (KR) was given verbally. The number of sums done was less in the sleep-deprived condition, although there was no difference in accuracy (see Figure 20a). The difference between the rested and sleep-deprived conditions was maximal in the third 5-minute period, while when KR was given in the last 5 minutes, there was no difference between the conditions. When rested, the subjects actually worked more slowly with KR than without it. It is possible that when subjects are already working as fast as they can, KR may merely prove a distraction.

Measurements were also made of the muscular tension, by recording the electromyographic potential (EMG). Subjects who showed least impairment of performance due to sleep loss also showed an increased level of EMG, while subjects who showed greatest impairment showed a decrease in EMG when suffering from loss of sleep. In both conditions, there was an increase in EMG when KR was given. This increase, however, was less when the subjects were sleep-deprived, so that the ratio of EMG for experimental to control conditions fell with KR (see Figure 20b). The EMG level is usually taken to be directly related to the level of arousal. Wilkinson felt that sleep loss resulted in a decrease in arousal, but that in a fairly active task, some subjects might exert more effort, when tired, to maintain their level of performance.

Wilkinson, Edwards and Haines (1966) varied the amount of

sleep taken on the night before testing. During the testing day, the subjects alternated between adding and vigilance tasks for a 14½ hour day. It was found that errors on the addition task remained low until sleep was reduced to one hour a night, but the speed of work was appreciably reduced following 3 hours' sleep. This experiment was carried on for 6 weeks, each subject receiving one sleep ration for two nights in a week (Wilkinson, 1968).

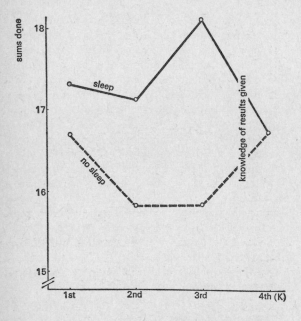

5 minute periods of the test

Figure 20a Speed of adding with and without sleep (from Wilkinson, 1962, p. 566)

Five-choice serial reaction task (see chapter 2). Pepler (1959) found that lack of sleep produced a decrease in the number of correct responses and an increase in the number of gaps (slow responses or blocks) when the task was self-paced. The number of gaps increased markedly over the 20 minutes of the task. Wilkinson (1959, 1961, 1963a and b) carried out an extensive investigation of the effects of sleep loss on this task. He confirmed Pepler's results and also found that 30-second breaks, every 5 minutes, heralded by a bell, prevented the

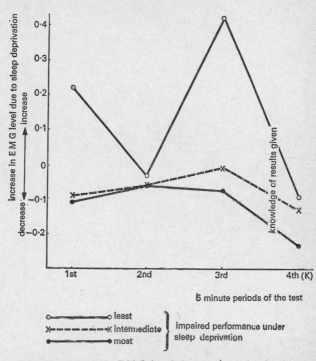

Figure 20b Increase in E M G level due to sleep deprivation, i.e. Log_{10} (no sleep E M G level/sleep E M G level) in three groups of Ss showing the least, the most, and an intermediate impairment of performance due to sleep deprivation (from Wilkinson, 1962, p. 566)

deterioration in the rate of correct responses, though the breaks did not significantly affect the number of gaps. The interactions of knowledge of results (K R), sleep and repeated testing were also studied (see Figure 21). The effect of lack of sleep *increased* for all measures as the subjects became more

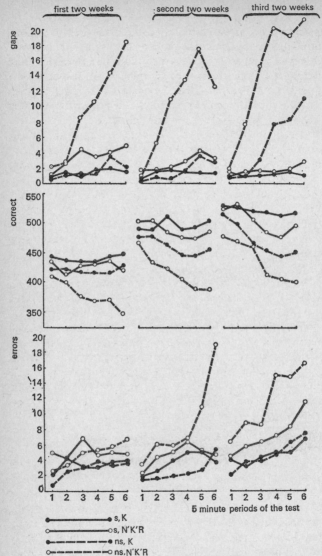

Figure 21 The effect of combination of sleep and no-sleep with knowledge of results (K R) and no knowledge of results (N K R) on gaps, corrects and errors in three successive and identical two week periods of testing (from Wilkinson, 1961, p. 265)

practiced. It was also found that subjects tended to respond more quickly and to make more errors in the later sessions. KR improved performance, especially with lack of sleep, but during the final sessions, decrements in all measures were found, even with KR, when the subjects were short of sleep. Thus, apparently the arousing effect of KR itself was reduced when subjects became more accustomed to it.

Wilkinson (1961) suggested that the nature of the fatigue may be the same whether the time spent on the task is continuous or intermittent. Habituation of the arousal response to the repetitive stimuli interacts with the sleepiness of the subjects deprived of sleep. As the task becomes more familiar, its arousing effect is reduced, even though the subjects may be getting better at it. Wilkinson pointed out that since in real life most tasks are highly familiar, effects of lack of sleep may be more marked than in unusual laboratory tasks in which the subject may be highly motivated.

Wilkinson (1963a) found that subjects who had a night's sleep following a night without sleep still showed more gaps than a control group.

Auditory noise may have an arousing effect and a distracting effect (see later). Wilkinson (1963b) found that there was an interaction between noise and sleep loss in their effects on performance in this self-paced reaction task (see Figure 22). Rested subjects performed less well when noise was added, but the performance of sleepless subjects was improved by the addition of noise.

(b) *Machine paced tracking tasks*

Pepler (1958, 1959) found that sleep loss tended to reduce activity and speed of performance in a tracking task, which required the subject to keep a pointer aligned to a slowly moving point, whose visibility was near threshold. Errors were increased as the task was continued, under the stresses of sleep loss and high temperatures. However, with sleep loss, this loss of accuracy was associated with a decrease in movements, while with high temperature there was an increase in movements.

Paced addition. Wilkinson (1964) described an adding task paced at speeds varying from 1 to 2 seconds per sum. On the second sleepless day there was a reduction in performance

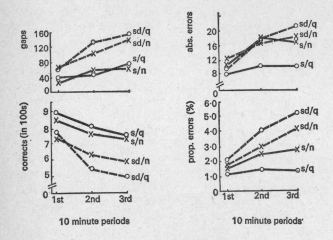

Figure 22 The effect of combinations of sleep (s) and sleep deprivation (sd) with noise (n) and quiet (q) upon: gaps, corrects, absolute errors, and proportional errors (errors as a percentage of all responses) (from Wilkinson, 1963b, p. 334)

which increased as the speed increased. Requiring the subject to add an extra eight to each sum made the slowest speed also very sensitive to sleep loss. Thus the decrement was due to a reduced speed of mental work and not to difficulties of intake or output.

Signal detection tasks. A task with a high signal frequency was studied by Williams, Lubin and Goodnow (1959; see also Williams, 1964). Letters were presented at a rate of one per second, and the signal was an X, which occurred sixteen times a minute. The task was either auditory or visual. There were very few errors with rested subjects, but a marked increase in errors with loss of sleep, especially with the auditory presentation. Errors increased rapidly over the first 4 minutes of the

10-minute task. The change was due to an increase in the longer reaction times. In other words, there was an increase in gaps, or blocks, with sleep loss. In a paced task such gaps show up as errors. Missed signals or prolonged reaction times coincided with periods in which the alpha rhythm was replaced by the theta rhythms characteristic of drowsiness.

(c) Vigilance tasks

Loss of sleep increases the rate of decrement in detections in vigilance tasks. Wilkinson (1960) studied a task in which the signal was a dim spot of light that could occur in any one of eight positions. He also recorded whether the subject was looking at the screen when a signal was given. He found that control subjects missed 20 per cent of signals while they were looking at the screen, while only 6 per cent were missed due to looking away from the screen. The sleep-deprived subjects missed 25 per cent when looking at the screen, 12 per cent when looking away from it, and 12 per cent because they were asleep, a total of almost 50 per cent, nearly twice as many as were missed by the rested subjects. The main effect of lack of sleep was to reduce the amount of time that the subject spent looking at the screen. Subjects who had a full night's sleep after a sleepless night also detected fewer signals than a control group (Wilkinson, 1963a), but the decrement during the session was the same for both groups. This result was similar to the increase in gaps found with the five-choice task under the same conditions (see p. 137).

The effect of varying the hours of sleep was studied in detail by Wilkinson, Edwards and Haines (1966; see also Wilkinson, 1968). The signal was a shorter tone in a series occurring at a rate of one every 2 seconds. There were forty signals per hour. A considerable reduction in detections was found when the subjects had received 3 hours' sleep or less on the previous night. False alarms showed a decrease as the previous night's sleep was reduced to 3 hours, but with further reduction there was an increase in false alarms. There was also a significant decrease in apparent sensitivity (d') as sleep was reduced beyond 3 hours. The criterial level (beta) showed much the same picture as did false reports, rising as sleep fell to 3 hours, and falling with further reduction in sleep. It has been found (see chapter 8) that false alarms may decrease less with depressant drugs than with stimulant drugs, while d′ may be reduced at the end of a vigilance session with depressant drugs, as compared with the stimulant amphetamine (Loeb *et al.*, 1965). It would seem that small reductions in the level of arousal mainly affect the criterion, but larger reductions affect sensitivity. This may be due to an increase in the variance of the spontaneous neural noise that results from the large slow waves of theta rhythm that are typical of drowsiness and sleep.

Continuous performance during a 24-hour vigilance task was examined by Baker, Ware and Sipowicz (1962). The task required the detection of a brief interruption of a continuous light source. The subjects showed a much slower decrement rate during this long watch than they did in an earlier 2-hour test. There was, however, a continuous decrement in detections during 17 hours, after which performance stabilized, except for those subjects who fell asleep (Figures 23a and b; see also Ware, Baker and Drucker, 1964).

Corcoran (1963) examined the effect of two nights' loss of sleep on a vigilance task requiring the detection of an odd-even-odd series of digits in a visual series presented at one or two digits per second. There were twenty signals in 30 minutes with the slow rate and forty with the fast rate. On the initial day's testing, performance was better with the slow rate, but following a night without sleep, the slow rate deteriorated more than the fast rate. This deterioration with the slow rate occurred between the first and second quarters of the test. On the third day, performance with the fast rate was better than the slow rate for both the sleepless and the control groups, but with the sleepless group, performance fell to a very low level with both rates. The initial advantage of the slow rate might have been due to the fact that all subjects were trained with the slow rate. Since the signal and background rates were altered together, it is difficult to discuss the results in terms of habituation or arousal. The decrement due to lack of

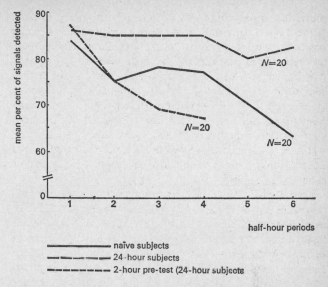

Figure 23a A comparison of mean per cent of signals detected during the first three hours of a 24-hour watch with the performance of a naïve control group in a 3-hour watch. Also shown is the performance of the 24-hour subjects during their 2-hour pre-test (from Baker, Ware and Sipowicz, 1962, p. 249)

sleep was remarkably large, detections reaching zero by the end of the third day's testing with the slow rate.

Physiological measures

During the digit-detection experiment, Corcoran (1964) also examined changes in heart rate. He found that there was a decline in heart rate throughout the first 3 days of testing in both sleepless and control groups. On the final day there was a further decline with the sleepless group, but the control group showed an increase. Corcoran suggested that this increase was due to the fact that the subjects were tested in the afternoon. He concluded that the subjects who had missed 2 nights' sleep showed a lower level of arousal than the controls. The reduction in heart rate from day to day both just before and

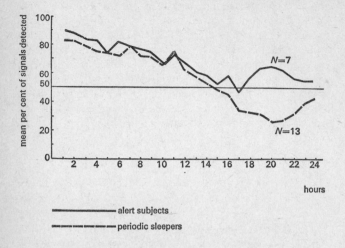

Figure 23b Mean per cent of signals detected over the 24-hour watch period (from Baker, Ware and Sipowicz, 1962, p. 247)

during the test represents habituation to the situation, as demonstrated by Glaser (1966). On the third day of testing, both detections and heart rate were reduced in the second half of the test.

While no attempt is being made to cover the field relating to sleep loss apart from its relation to performance in continuous tasks, some other physiological data are of interest in relation to the problem of arousal. Frohman and Luby (1964) reported that there was a rise in energy production of the red blood cells over the first 48 hours of sleep deprivation, followed by a fall. During the first 48 hours there was also found paroxysmal high voltage spiking of EEG. Later this disappeared and 'paradoxical' alpha was seen (see p. 95).

Ax and Luby (1961) found that declines in central sympathetic activity, as measured by palmar sweating and GSR, occurred during sleep loss, indicating a decline in arousal. Whether the sympathetic nervous system reaction is the cause or result of reticular activation is not yet determined. Baust and Niemczyk (1964) have suggested that the effect of adrenalin on the reticular system may be mediated by the blood pressure. Frohman and Luby (1964) likewise concluded that sympathetic activity early in sleep deprivation utilized high-energy phosphate in order to sustain arousal. In later stages, periods of drowsiness may allow replenishment of the energy stores. Like all brain functions, it is probable that there is a homeostatic mechanism that attempts to maintain arousal at a level that is consistent with the general functioning of the body.

EEG changes

Over-all measures of the amount of alpha rhythm or the amount of high-frequency low-amplitude rhythm present in the EEG may give misleading results (see p. 94). If a stimulus leads to the appearance of the alpha rhythm, then the background level of arousal is likely to be low, even though the EEG contains mostly low-amplitude high-frequency patterns.

Tyler, Goodman and Rothman (1947) found that there was an increase in higher frequencies as sleep deprivation increased. On the other hand, Williams, Lubin and Goodnow (1959) found that errors of omission were related to the replacement of the alpha rhythm by the theta rhythm of drowsiness.

Conclusions

There is an interaction between sleep deprivation and time on task, so that the detrimental effect of sleep deprivation increases with time on task. In a vigilance task, subjects may actually fall asleep during the session. Small reductions in sleep may enhance the customary decrease in false alarms, but larger reductions in sleep may result in an increase in false alarms or positive errors. Further work is needed on the relationship between the background EEG, the neural response to the repetitive stimulus, and performance with varying levels of lack of sleep. It is possible that the first change is a replacement of the alpha rhythm by the low-amplitude rhythm, and then the large-amplitude theta waves appear. The first change might decrease false alarms and the second increase them.

B. Noise

The term 'noise' is being used here in its original sense, to mean a loud auditory stimulus. In most experiments it also means a random, meaningless stimulus containing equal energy at all audio frequencies, known as 'white' noise. Unless otherwise mentioned, the noise is continuous throughout the session.

Noise may have both an arousing effect and a distracting effect. It is possible to explain the harmful effects of noise by distraction or by the inverted-U curve relating arousal to performance. Too high levels of arousal are then called hyper-arousal (Freeman, 1940; Hebb, 1955; see also Poulton, 1966, who has given a summary of reports of the effect of noise on performance). The two explanations may be brought together by assuming that an increase in arousal is only beneficial until the alert level of brain rhythms is reached. Beyond this point, further sympathetic changes may prove distracting. Thus tremor, sweating, rapid and emphatic heart beat and pupillary dilation leading perhaps to dazzle and glare may all interfere with accurate performance. The distinction by Sokolov (1963) between the defence reaction and the orienting reaction is relevant here.

If the task is one producing low arousal, like a vigilance task, or if the subject is in a state of drowsiness due to lack of sleep, then noise may improve performance.

Broadbent (1958) has summarized the effect of noise as follows:

1. The transient effects of noise. The sudden onset of a noise may produce very brief declines in efficiency, which disappear as the noise continues (see Woodhead, 1964a and b). Broadbent suggested that here the noise was acting as a distracting stimulus, to which attention was paid because it was novel.

2. A loud (100 decibels) high-pitched noise produces brief intermittent perceptual failures of performance. Broadbent

demonstrated an inhibitory effect of noise on detections of criterial changes in the twenty-dial test. Out of fifteen critical signals presented in $1\frac{1}{2}$ hours, five were detected in the control condition and three in the presence of noise. When twenty lights were used as the source of easily seen signals, the effect of noise disappeared. Jerison (1957, 1963) found that noise caused a decrement in detection of signals presented on three clocks, but did not affect detection when only one clock was used. Broadbent pointed out that tasks showing an effect of noise often required the regular shifting of attention from one source to another. He also emphasized that noise (like loss of sleep) might only show its harmful effects after a period of work (see also a recent review by Mirabella and Goldstein, 1967, on the effects of noise on signal detection).

Five-choice task

Broadbent (1953) found that noise increased the number of errors in the five-choice task. At the beginning of the test, performance was better in noise than in quiet, but errors increased more rapidly in noise. Corcoran (1962; see Figure 24) examined the interactions between noise and sleep deprivation. He found that gaps increased more rapidly with lack of sleep than with the control subjects, but noise reduced this effect of sleep loss. There was a similar effect on the rate of correct responses. These were reduced by lack of sleep, and increased by noise. Errors were not affected by either variable. Thus in this task the only effect of noise was to counteract the effect of sleep loss. It would appear that the 90 decibels noise exerted an arousing effect, which was maximal when the sleep-deprived subjects were habituated to the task.

Wilkinson (1963b) reported a further experiment on the interactions between noise, lack of sleep and knowledge of results on the five-choice task. The findings can be summarized as follows (see Figure 22):

1. There was an interaction between the effects of sleep deprivation and noise. With the sleep-deprived subjects, there was less decrement in performance during the session with noise than without it. This applied to gaps and proportional errors,

both of which increased during the session, and also to the rate of correct responses, which decreased. With the rested subjects, noise increased the error rate, especially towards the end of the task. Noise did not affect the gap rate with rested subjects.

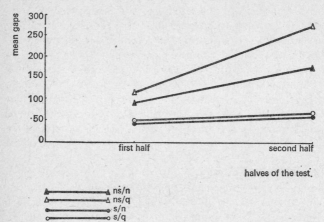

Figure 24 The effects of lack of sleep (ns) and noise (n) on performance in the serial reaction task. A gap is a period greater than $1\frac{1}{2}$ seconds between successive responses in the unpaced task (from Corcoran, 1962, p. 181)

2. There was also an interaction between the effects of knowledge of results and noise. Noise had more of an adverse effect on performance when KR was present than when it was absent. This was particularly seen in the scores for gaps and errors. Gaps increased more rapidly when noise was added to KR than when KR was given alone, although both conditions showed fewer gaps than when KR was not given. In the control condition without KR, noise slightly decreased gaps, and had no effect on errors.

Wilkinson interpreted his results as suggesting that noise was arousing, while sleep loss reduced arousal. Knowledge of results also increased arousal, and time on task decreased it. Thus, sleep-deprived subjects showed poorest performance at the end of a session, while noise and K R both improved this deteriorated performance. Adding noise to K R with normal subjects reduced the effect of K R given alone. This effect Wilkinson interpreted as being due to hyper-arousal. He also found that the effect of noise interacted with the familiarity of the task. Noise increased errors with practiced subjects, but not with naïve subjects. In this interaction, noise resembled sleep loss, which had a greater effect with practiced subjects.

There are some difficulties in the conception of the deleterious effects of noise being due to hyper-arousal. Why should its effect appear later in the session, and why should they appear when the task is more familiar? Under these circumstances it would appear that the interference effect of noise might be due to distraction. When the novelty of the task stimuli has worn off, then the distracting effect of the noise might be more powerful.

Broadbent (1958) suggested that the effects of noise might be due to changes in the direction of attention. There were two postulates in this theory: (1) The brain has a limited capacity, and by means of a filter selects a part of the incoming information for processing; (2) Certain properties of the stimulus lead to its selection; these are physical intensity, biological importance and novelty. It may be noted that these properties are also those that lead to an increased arousal or orienting response. The orienting response has both a generalized tonic component and a specific phasic component. The first may be regarded as related to the overall level of arousal, while the second may be regarded as related to the distribution of attention, as discussed by Broadbent. When the neural response to a repetitive event has habituated, then the attention may select other stimuli. Many other factors may also govern the distribution of attention, such as set, motivation, expectancy and so on. Explanations in terms of a one-dimensional continuum of arousal do not seem to be adequate. A combined filter-arousal theory seems necessary, as pointed out by McGrath (1963a).

As a result of habituation of the responses to the events of the task, attention may turn towards other stimuli, such as noise; the subject may go on making responses, but more of these responses will be errors. This effect may be more apparent when the subject is familiar with the task and is working faster. On the other hand, when he is suffering from loss of sleep, moments of drowsiness may result in gaps; and the arousing effect of noise or knowledge of results may improve performance by eliminating these gaps.

Vigilance tasks

The experiments by Broadbent and by Jerison on stimuli from multiple sources have been described (see p. 145). Corcoran (1962) examined the effect of noise and sleep deprivation on the visual digit task, where the signal was a series of three odd numbers in succession. This signal occurred twenty times in the 30 minutes of the test. He found that sleep-deprived subjects missed more signals than the controls, particularly towards the end of the task. Noise had no significant effect, but there was an interaction between the three variables of sleep, periods of the task and noise (see Figures 25a and b). For the first three-quarters of the test, the noise increased the difference between sleep-deprived and rested subjects, but in the final quarter, this was not so. This difference was found because, in the final quarter, more signals were missed by the rested subjects when noise was present than when it was not, while with the sleep-deprived subjects, noise made no difference in the final quarter.

Again these results might be interpreted on the assumption that the distraction effect of noise increased during the session. This effect was, however, only seen with the rested subjects, because with the sleep-deprived subjects the arousal effect of noise counteracted its distraction effect at the end of the session.

Dardano (1962) found that when visual signals were presented with a low variability of intersignal interval (50–70 seconds) reaction times were much shorter than when the inter-signal interval was more variable. The non-signal events occurred once every ten seconds, so that it would be easy for the subjects to determine the probability of a signal by count-

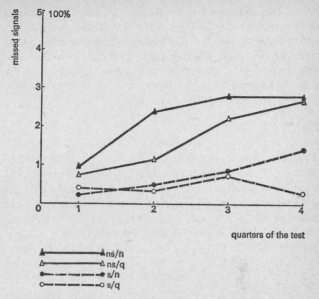

Figure 25a The effect of lack of sleep (ns) and noise (n) on detection of three successive odd numbers in a visual series. Above is the average performance, in the four quarters of the 30-minute test. (from Corcoran, 1962, p. 179)

ing the non-signal events. When an intermittent noise was added to this task, there was a considerable increase in reaction time. Dardano suggested that the noise might have interfered with the ability of the subjects to estimate time, which seems very probable, since the bursts of noise varied from 30 seconds to 3 minutes in duration.

With increased variability of intersignal interval, Dardano found that the reaction time was increased, but the effect of noise was reduced. With the maximum variability of intersignal interval, the noise had no effect. In this condition, there was an increase in the very long reaction times, and a decrease in shorter reaction times as the session continued. Measures of basal skin conductance were taken during this high variability condition. Subjects who showed an increase in reaction time during the session also showed a decrease in conductance, suggesting that there was a decrease in arousal. There was no evidence that noise affected basal skin conductance, a measure showing very great variation between subjects.

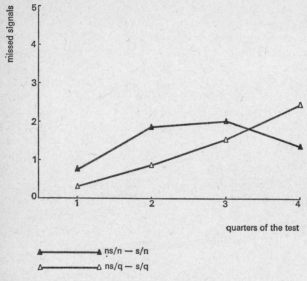

quarters of the test

▲————————▲ ns/n — s/n
△————————△ ns/q — s/q

Figure 25b The difference between performance with and without sleep (from Corcoran, 1962, p. 179)

Broadbent and Gregory (1963b) carried out an investigation of the effects of noise on a visual vigilance task in terms of signal detection theory. They found that towards the end of the session the risky or doubtful criterion became more cautious in noise than in quiet. In this task there were three lights flashing simultaneously every 1·4 seconds for 0·3 second. The signal was a slightly brighter flash on any one tube. A 100-decibel noise was given on one condition. At the beginning the noise had no effect. In the last half-hour there was a significant improvement in d' in noise with the most risky criterion but not with the most cautious. There were no significant changes in detections. The authors suggested that

noise and prolonged work might produce differential effects
on the values of hits and false positives.

This work was continued in a later report (Broadbent and
Gregory, 1965). There were either one or three lights on which
a signal might occur, and the signal rate was either one in five
or one in fifteen flashes; that is, $3 \cdot 4$ or $1 \cdot 1$ signals per minute.
In each of the three display conditions the initial level of 'sure'
detections was higher in noise than in quiet, and the initial
level of false detections was about the same or slightly lower in
noise. On the other hand, the final level of 'sure' detections
and false reports was about the same in both cases. Thus it
would appear that the noise originally improved the sensitivity
of the subject for the signal, when he used a strict criterion,
but this effect wore off. 'Unsure' detections were significantly
lower in noise than in quiet, except with the low signal rate.
In the final period of the session with a high signal frequency
on one channel, the number of signals receiving a 'sure'
negative response was significantly greater in noise than in
quiet. This was not the case with the low signal frequency.
Broadbent and Gregory suggested that the harmful effect of
noise at the end of a session was due to a fall in the number of
doubtful responses.

Davies and Hockey (1966) examined the interactions between noise, signal rate and temperament in a visual digit
cancellation task. Subjects had to check a typescript against
a series of digits appearing on a television screen (see p. 117).
There was no decrement in detections under the noise condition, but in quiet the extraverts showed a decrement. Introverts gave more false alarms in quiet than in noise, but
extraverts gave more in noise than in quiet. There was a
tendency for d' to increase during the session with introverts,
especially with noise. Beta increased during all sessions but
showed its greatest increase in the noise sessions with the
introverts and in the quiet sessions with the extraverts (private
communication). The authors discussed these results in terms
of the U-shaped curve of arousal, on the assumption that in
any condition the introverts would be more aroused than the
extraverts, and noise and a high signal rate would be more

arousing than quiet and a low signal rate. They pointed out that this explanation would not fit the data for false alarms. Changes in false alarms during a session may not be related to changes in arousal but to changes in expectancy (see Mackworth, 1970). It should be noted that this task involved active scanning from screen to typescript. In such tasks there may be considerable learning (see Colquhoun, 1966).

The nature of the noise

The effect of extraneous noise depends on the nature of the noise. Meaningful sounds such as music and speech may have different effects from white noise. Tarrière and Wisner (1962) examined the effects of four environmental conditions on performance in a vigilance task. These conditions were 90-decibel noise, silence, classical music and jokes. The subjects watched a projection of a scene representing the view from a car while driving along a forest road. They had to detect small lights that appeared eight times each half-hour. There was a decrement in detections in all conditions, and a considerable improvement from day to day.

The results are shown in Figure 26. Best performance was found with the music. Comparison of noise with quiet showed that there was an initially beneficial effect of the noise over the first hour, but the performance in noise fell to a level below that in silence. The jokes had a differential effect depending on the state of practice. The first session showed an interference with detection, but with practiced subjects, jokes produced an improvement. Thus it appears that music had an arousing effect throughout, while noise may have had some arousing effect initially, but later the distracting effect was dominant. Since the music was continually changing, while the noise was not, this difference is to be expected. The jokes provided a distracting effect when the subject was learning the task, but an arousing effect when the task did not require so much attention.

McGrath (1963a and b) carried out a similar investigation into the effects of variety noise, as compared with white noise, on detection in a visual vigilance task. Since he was mainly

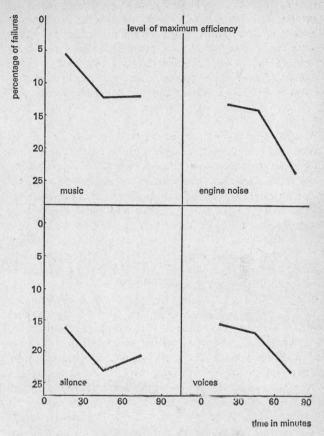

Figure 26 Percentage of omissions by thirty-five subjects in a visual vigilance task under conditions with different ambient auditory stimulation (from Tarrière and Wisner, 1962, p. 13)

interested in the arousal effects of the variety noise, he kept the sound level to 71 decibels, a level not expected to have harmful effects on performance. Subjects were required to detect small increments in the brightness of an intermittent light. The variety audio consisted of music, talk, traffic sounds and so on. He found that more signals were detected with the variety audio than with the noise, when the *event* rate was twenty per minute. When the event rate was increased to sixty per minute, detection was greatly reduced in both conditions (Mackworth, 1970). The condition with variety audio suffered more than that with noise.

McGrath interpreted these results in terms of the filter-arousal theory. He assumed that variety audio increased the rate of selection of irrelevant information, but also retarded the loss of arousal. He also offered a simpler explanation, that on an easy task, arousing conditions improve performance, while on a difficult task they are harmful. Detailed interpretations of this kind of experiment are difficult without a knowledge of false alarms. Jerison, Pickett and Stenson (1965; see chapter 9) have pointed out that the event rate may affect the criterion of the subject rather than his ability to detect the signal.

If habituation of the response to the repetitive event occurs more rapidly when the event rate is higher, then it might be expected that more attention would be paid to the meaningful audio. The difference between the two conditions with the fast event rate was maximal in the second quarter-hour of the session. This would be expected if habituation and distraction were the major causes of this early decrement. This is simply a restatement of the filter-arousal explanation offered by McGrath.

A similar experiment was carried out by Kirk and Hecht (1963). The signal was a deflection of a spot on a cathode ray tube. There were three environmental conditions: quiet, and constant or variable noise. These three conditions were presented to the subject in successive 10-minute periods of the 2-hour test, in which 60 signals were given. It was found that in the second hour, detections were significantly better during the variable noise than in either of the other two conditions.

Variable noise was given by McBain (1961) in an active but monotonous hand-printing task. Subjects were required to print a series of fourteen letters, at a rate that was paced at three-fifths of their rate in a self-paced pre-test. The noise was a tape of speech and other sounds played backwards. It was found that there were significantly fewer errors with noise, but the rate of increase of errors during the session was unaffected by noise.

C. Sensory Deprivation

Performance on a modified clock test was examined by Zubek, Pushkar, Sansom and Gowing (1961) after the subjects had been lying on a mattress in a dark and soundproofed room for 7 days. They were tested after they emerged from the deprivation conditions. There was a significant decrease in detections. A slowing of the occipital EEG rhythms was also found (see also Zubek, 1964). Zubek and MacNeill (1966) found the same slowing of EEG activity in subjects who were immobilized for a week but not otherwise deprived. They were tested with a combined visual and auditory vigilance task before and after the week of immobilization. Their performance was also compared with control subjects, some of whom were tested normally and others in the recumbent position. The experimental subjects detected most visual signals when tested after the week of immobilization. Their performance was better than in the pre-test, and also better than either of the control groups. Detection of the auditory signals was slightly worse after the week of immobilization, and worse than the normal controls, but significantly better than the recumbent controls (see Figure 27). The authors pointed out that other workers had also found an increase in visual acuity after several days of perceptual isolation (e.g. Doane et al., 1959). Friel and Derogatis (1965) found that after only 50 minutes of non-pattern deprivation, subjects could recognize words at shorter exposure times than controls.

Smith, Myers and Murphy (1967) tested subjects during perceptual isolation, instead of after emerging. They presented a 0·1 second tone which was readily audible. The experimental subjects were in the dark at all times. Their response to the signals was significantly faster than that of the controls, especially in the second half of the test. Control subjects who were tested in the dark showed the slowest performance of all. The usual increase in latency during the session was found with all subjects, except in the first test with the experimental subjects. Similar relationships were found with the few missed signals.

Smith *et al.* (1967) suggested that the deprived subjects showed hyper-aroused behaviour, and that when returned to normal environments might be suffering from sensory overload. When tested during deprivation, the signals would be more arousing, due to contrast with the previous conditions. These experiments suggest that 'the readiness to detect and

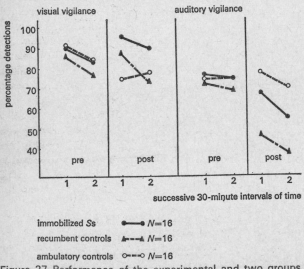

immobilized *Ss*   ●——● *N*=16

recumbent controls   ▲---▲ *N*=16

ambulatory controls   ○---○ *N*=16

Figure 27 Performance of the experimental and two groups of control subjects on visual and auditory vigilance in terms of percentage detection of 'signal' changes occurring in two successive 30-minute intervals of time. Subjects tested before and after the experimental conditions (from Zubek and MacNeill, 1966, p. 325)

respond to signals' is improved during sensory deprivation, and emphasize the difference between the over-all level of arousal and the arousing effect of a stimulus. The latter may be increased when the former is low.

Summary

Loss of sleep probably reduces the over-all level of arousal of the subject, while noise may have two effects, a distracting effect and an arousing effect. The latter may be increased when variable noise or music is employed. While some of the data on noise may be explained on the basis of the U-shaped curve relating arousal level and performance, such an explanation cannot deal with the finding that the harmful effect of noise may be greatest at the end of a monotonous task.

The effect of sleep loss may also be most apparent at the end of the session, when the arousal response to the repetitive stimuli has been reduced by habituation. Noise tends to counteract the effects of loss of sleep, but sleep loss does not improve performance when noise is present. The effect of sleep loss is greater when the task has become more familiar. It tends to decrease the speed of performance and to increase gaps in a continuous task. In a vigilance task there may be a more rapid decrease in detections. Noise tends to increase errors in a continuous task, while in a vigilance task it appears to reduce the number of doubtful decisions. Presumably, in a continuous task the subject makes a response even when his attention is distracted, while in the vigilance task he tends to assume that the more probable non-signal event has occurred.

When subjects are suffering from loss of sleep, they may actually fall asleep during a vigilance task. False alarms, however, may decrease with small amounts of sleep loss, but increase again with greater deprivation. Thus, the initial effect of sleep loss would seem to resemble the usual vigilance decrement, namely, there is an increase in caution, but greater amounts of sleep loss may decrease sensitivity.

Knowledge of results counteracts the effects of sleep loss, and the effects of continued performance, but noise may reduce the effect of knowledge of results. While this finding might be explained by the U-shaped relation between arousal and performance, the harmful effect of noise given with knowledge of results should have been maximal at the beginning of the session. Instead it increased towards the end of the session.

It is clear that the effect of noise upon vigilance performance requires further study. The maximum harmful effect is obtained with continuous very loud noise given with tasks involving scanning and in active tasks such as the five-choice task, suggesting that it is due to distraction, which increases as the neural response to the events of the task habituates.

Sensory deprivation may increase sensitivity for signals in a vigilance task, when subjects are tested without a change in the deprived environment. This may be due to the increased arousal response produced by the signals, resulting from maximum contrast with the environment. Alternatively, it may arise from the fact that subjects have had so much sleep that they are in the opposite condition to the sleep-deprived subjects, though the term hyper-aroused, with its connotation of reduced performance, would not seem to be appropriate.

8 Temperature, Drugs and Other Stresses

A. Temperature

N. H. Mackworth (1950) investigated the effect of environmental temperature upon performance in the clock test. Subjects were acclimatized by 2 weeks of daily exposure to heat for 2 hours. Each subject was tested at one of four temperatures, ranging from 70° to 97°F on the Effective Temperature scale. Fewest signals were missed at 79°F (E T) than at the cooler or hotter temperatures. At the hotter temperatures, there was an increased rate of decrement during the 2-hour sessions. Mackworth suggested that the lowest temperature was uncomfortably cold for these subjects, who were dressed only in shorts, and had been acclimatized to much hotter temperatures.

Mackworth (1950) also examined the effect of environmental high temperatures on heavy physical work (the pull test). He found that the amount of work done was greatly increased by giving knowledge of results, that it deteriorated with high temperatures, and that this deterioration with temperature was greater under the knowledge of results condition. Moreover, maximum deterioration was found with those subjects who performed best. It would seem that the limiting factor with the normal temperatures was psychological rather than physical, but at high temperatures, physical factors were important. In a wireless telegraphy task, Mackworth found the greatest effect of high temperature on performance by least skilled subjects (Figure 28).

Further analyses of the effects of environmental temperature were reported by Pepler (1958, 1959, 1960). The initial experiments were carried out at Singapore, where the subjects

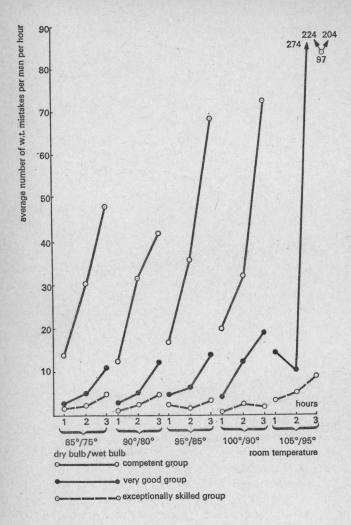

Figure 28 Wireless telegraphy test: Effect of level of ability during prolonged watches at high atmospheric temperatures (from N. H. Mackworth, 1950; 1961 edn, p. 139)

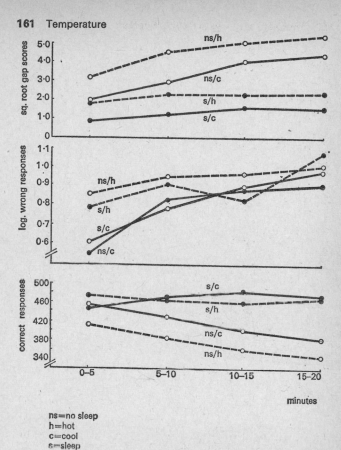

ns=no sleep
h=hot
c=cool
s=sleep

Figure 29a Changes in scores during prolonged serial choice (from Pepler, 1959, p. 448)

were already acclimatized to high temperatures. He confirmed the results of Mackworth with a manual tracking task and the clock test, but found that the optimal temperature was at 82° F (ET). Pepler (1959) investigated the interactions between warmth and sleep loss in the manual tracking task and the five-choice task (Figure 29a and b). Both heat and sleep loss increased errors in the tracking task and gaps in the five-choice task. There were certain differences between the effects

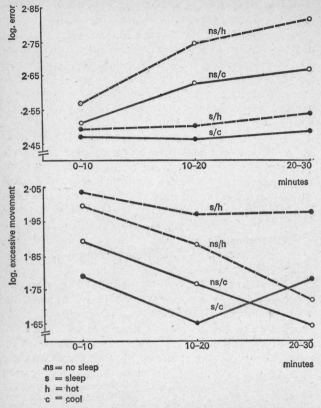

ns = no sleep
s = sleep
h = hot
c = cool

Figure 29b Changes in scores during prolonged tracking (from Pepler, 1959, p. 448)

of sleep and heat. The effect of heat was uniform throughout the test, while sleep loss increased the rate of decrement. Heat produced excessive movements of the pointer in the tracking task, particularly in rested subjects; heat also increased the number of wrong responses in the five-choice task, but here the effect was greater with the sleepless subjects. Sleep loss decreased the number of correct responses in the five-choice task. This effect was intensified by heat. Pepler concluded that heat reduced the ability of the subject to make the correct response, while sleep loss reduced his reactivity.

Pepler (1960) suggested that the effect of warmth was not due to distraction, because glare and quiet speech, which should cause distraction, decreased movements in the tracking task, while heat increased such excessive movements. All conditions increased errors. Pepler suggested that environmental heat may reduce an individual's ability to execute accurately timed and graded movements.

Very severe stress due to heat, noise and vibration was employed by Loeb and Jeantheau (1958) by testing subjects on Broadbent's twenty dials task in an Army troop carrier. The temperature during the day reached 125°F. It was found that heat alone had no detrimental effect. When the carrier was moving, so that noise and vibration were considerable, there was an increase in reaction time, both in the day and in the night tests. In the day, this triple stress produced a very large increase in reaction time fairly early in the testing, but performance soon improved.

Mackworth (1950) found no reliable relationship between body temperature and performance. Bell, Provins and Hiorns (1964) found that more signals were missed in an auditory vigilance task when the body temperature was higher, although there were no significant differences in detection between different climates up to 145°/117°F. A controlled study of the relation between body temperature and performance in an auditory vigilance task and an adding test was carried out by Wilkinson et al., (1964). Each task lasted for 21 minutes. The subject knew that there would be ten signals in the session of 21 minutes. The body temperatures were raised by exposing the subject nude to a hot humid climate. When he had reached the desired temperature, he was removed from the hot environment and dressed in a thin vapor-barrier suit, through which air was passed to maintain the temperature at the required level, while the subject sat in a room at 37°C. On control days the mean body temperature was 36·5°C. The raised temperatures were 37·3°, 37·9° and 38·5°C (101·5°F).

Each subject was tested for sixteen days. In each 4-day

period each subject was tested at the three raised temperatures followed by the control day. More signals were detected and the response time was shorter as the body temperature was raised. The rate of detection decreased over days, particularly in the control tests. In the first 4-day period, there was a marked difference (Figures 30a and b). There was a fall in detections over the successive tests with the control condition.

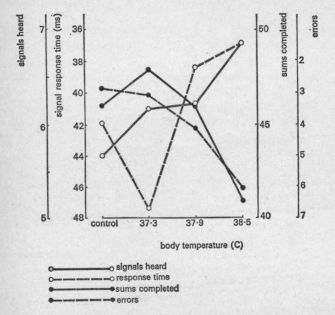

Figure 30a Comparison of the mean performance scores in two successive 21-minute tests: an auditory vigilance task and an adding task; scores averaged over 12 days (from Wilkinson *et al.,* 1964, p. 290)

The difference between the control condition at 36·5°C and 37·3°C in the last 4-day period is quite remarkable.

In the adding test, most sums were completed at the slightly raised body temperature of 37·3°C and fewest at 38·5°C. There was an improvement over successive 4-day periods at all the behavioural measures of motor activity. This is particularly noticeable with atropine and its analogues, such as benactyzine and hyoscine. Atropine leads to high-voltage slow EEG patterns similar to those characteristic of sleep, but the animals may be fully awake, and even jump off the table. In this context, it may be pointed out that many depressants act first on the inhibitory functions, so that an early stage of intoxication by alcohol or nitrous oxide may be marked by excitability.

The following classification of drugs is modified from Elkes (1961):

Group I. The sympatheticomimetic drugs, such as amphetamine, produce both behavioural and EEG arousal patterns. Amphetamine is believed to act via the reticular activating system.

Group II. Chlorpromazine and similar drugs produce a slight rise in the threshold for arousal produced by stimulation of the reticular formation, but a marked rise in threshold to arousal produced by clicks. The threshold for single click responses in the auditory cortex was unchanged. These drugs block the effects of amphetamine. Mirsky and Kornetsky (1964) suggested that chlorpromazine acts directly on the reticular formation, while the barbituates act primarily on the cortex and interfere with subcortical structures. (See also ster and Guerrero-Figueroa, 1966.)

up III. Atropine, hyoscine and benactyzine produce a ciation between EEG and motor activity. The EEG ns are those of sleep: that is, slow waves of high amplit the same time, there may be considerable motor There is a marked rise in the threshold of arousal d by direct stimulation of the reticular system. Ostfeld, nd Unna (1960) found a decrease in all measures of th atropine, except the pulse rate, which increased. a decrease in spontaneous speech and movement, ssion of the EEG arousal response to repetitive lation.

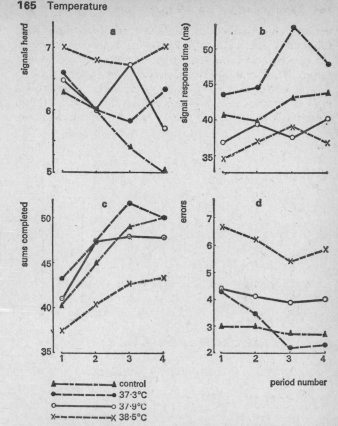

Figure 30b Changes in performance scores between the four periods of testing at the four body temperature levels. (a) signals heard in vigilance tests. (b) response time in vigilance test. (c) sums completed in adding test. (d) errors made in adding test (from Wilkinson *et al.*, 1964, p. 290)

temperatures. The marked increase in errors at the highest temperature agrees with the results found by Pepler. Wilkinson *et al.*, (1964) suggested that raised body temperature increased arousal, so that subjects were hyper-aroused in the active adding task, but with the monotonous vigilance task, performance was improved by high temperatures. On the other hand, Pepler found a summation of the effects of heat and sleep loss on errors.

It is doubtful whether a single continuum of arousal is sufficient to explain all the data. The complexity of the various factors was shown by Poulton and Kerslake (1965), who examined performance in a listening task and a dial watching task at effective temperatures of 86° and 65°. On the first day, efficiency was reliably better in the warmth than in the cool environment, but these levels of performance were maintained when the subjects received the tests in the other temperature on the second day. Thus, there were no over-all differences between the environments. The psychological effects of learning the task in a more comfortable environment persisted when the environment was changed.

The effects of cold

Very little work has been done on the effect of cold on mental tasks. Mackworth, Pepler, and Poulton and Kerslake found that performance was adversely affected by temperatures only slightly below the optimum, when subjects were inadequately dressed. Poulton, Hitchings and Brooke (1965) carried out a field test in the Arctic. Subjects sat on the open bridge of a ship and were required to respond to dim lights separated by an angle of 75°. The measure of performance was the number of responses delayed for 2 seconds or longer. The results showed that there were reliably more delayed responses to signals at the end of the task than to signals near the beginning. No such trend was found under milder conditions. In the Arctic, the body temperature fell to 96·2°F (35·7°C) even though the subjects were wearing Arctic suits.

Optimum performance on the pursuit rotor was found at 75°F by Teichner and Kobrick (1955) and Teichner and Wehrkamp (1954). Accuracy was reduced at both 55° and 85°F. When exposure to 55°F followed prolonged training at 75°F, there was an immediate reduction in performance to the initial level found at the beginning of training. Continued training over 12 days at 55° led to an improvement which did not reach the previous maximum seen at 75°. When the

subjects returned to 75°, performance immediately returned to the high level attained at this temperature earlier. In this experiment subjects were kept for the whole twenty-four hours of each testing day at the particular temperature at which the testing was carried out. Thus, it appeared that cold had an immediate, harmful effect, which was gradually reduced as the subjects became acclimatized.

It would seem possible that all the brain processes would be slowed at lower body temperatures and speeded up at higher temperatures. This might increase the speed of reaction at higher temperatures. It might also affect the ability of the subject to estimate time intervals. At higher temperatures the subjects might estimate a time interval as longer than it really was. Consequently, he might expect more signals in a given period of time than when tested at a lower temperature. This might result in a more lax criterion. Speculation on the possible causes of the observed changes due to environmental and body temperature must await experiments examining neurological changes and criterial levels.

It can be concluded that there is an optimal level of temperature for performance on prolonged and monotonous tasks such as vigilance. Cold may slow reactions and interfere with detections, especially at the beginning of exposure. Heat may lead to increased errors and excessive overshooting in a tracking task, and to increased missed signals in a vigilance task, especially towards the end of a long session. It is probable that a rise in temperature speeds up all the physiological processes, so that the results obtained vary considerably, depending on the processes involved.

B. Drugs

The effect of drugs on measures of arousal

An excellent summary of the effect of drugs on arousal has been written by not all measures are affected can be complete dissociation

Group IV. Physostigmine produces effects opposite to those of atropine, leading to a fall of threshold for the EEG arousal pattern but little change in behavioural threshold.

Group V. Reserpine does not affect arousal thresholds for direct electrical stimulation, but in large doses it may produce the activation pattern in the EEG.

Group VI. Meprobamate has little effect on arousal thresholds. Other workers, however, have found that this drug produces changes in the EEG similar to the effects of barbiturates (Henry and Obrist, 1958).

Group VII. Barbiturates produce a depressant effect on the pathways subserving wakefulness. They slow a synergistic action with chlorpromazine. They produce the characteristic slow waves of sleep in the EEG. They reduce the variance of the amplitude of the cortical evoked response (Brazier, 1964). Thompson (1967, p. 220) describes how barbiturates may increase the initial positive wave of the specific auditory evoked potential but completely eliminate later components. Barbiturate anaesthesia also eliminates the evoked responses from the association areas (see pp. 69, 87). Chloralose anaesthesia does not have this effect.

Elkes suggested that response to stress may be shown as either overactivity due to the faltering of a physiological braking mechanism, or as underactivity resulting from excessive inhibitory tone, which in its turn results from a runaway excitatory process (see also p. 100). This statement illustrates clearly the complexity of the processes involved in arousal. Neither guesses nor logic can determine what is happening, only detailed experiments can give the final answer. Elkes pointed out that drugs act by shifting the balance in processes which normally regulate interactions between widely scattered neural nets.

The effect of drugs on performance

Because of the probable relation between arousal and

performance, the effect of stimulant and depressant drugs on performance has aroused considerable interest.

Stimulants. Amphetamine has effects similar to those of adrenalin on the central nervous system. It appears to act through the reticular system, producing behavioural arousal and desynchronizing the E E G pattern (French, 1960, p. 1291). Eserine also produces arousal, but may inhibit the alerting effect of amphetamine. Barnes (1966) has suggested that there are two separate systems, adrenergic and cholinergic, both of which may produce arousal.

Amphetamine appears to act mainly by preventing the decline in performance resulting from continued work or from sleep loss. It is probable that it prevents habituation of the arousal response or orienting reaction. There is considerable evidence that amphetamine increases the output of behaviour that normally has a low frequency of occurrence, and decreases the output of high-frequency behaviour (C. B. Smith, 1964). Hearst and Whalen (1963) found that amphetamine produced a two-fold increase in avoidance responses, and also *decreased* non-stimulus responses. Thus, amphetamine might be expected to maintain the rate of observing responses, without increasing false alarms.

There is evidence that amphetamine lowers the two-flash threshold (Kopell, Noble and Silverman, 1965). Venables (1963) suggested that the subjective threshold of fusion of two successive flashes of light might be related to the level of arousal, since there was a relation between skin conductance and the two-flash threshold.

A review of the effects of caffeine and amphetamine on the performance has been presented by Weiss and Laties (1962). They concluded that a very wide range of behaviour can be enhanced by these drugs, and that this improvement was at least partly due to a direct effect upon performance, although there might also be motivational changes. Talland and Quarton (1966) also summarized the data and reported an experiment which demonstrated an absolute improvement of sustained attention with methamphetamine. Signals (the numeral four) appeared at an average rate of eleven per minute, and were on view for 1 to 3 seconds in displays consisting of up to nine numerals. It was found that in the second session, performance was significantly better with amphetamine than with a placebo, especially towards the end of the session. Though there was no significant effect of drugs on false responses, there were fewer with amphetamine.

Tracking tasks. The effect of drugs on the multidimensional pursuit test was extensively investigated by Payne and Hauty (see chapter 2). In this task, the subject has to keep the pointers on four dials properly aligned. Payne and Hauty (1954) found that during the first 2 hours of testing, performance continued to improve when amphetamine had been given, in contrast to the rapid decrement found in the control condition. After this, the level of performance with the stimulant declined at more or less the same rate as the control. They found that different kinds of instructions had no effect on performance. Hauty and Payne (1955) reported that when the subjects were told that they would have a rest after 4 hours, performance was better throughout than when they were told that they would be working for 7 hours, though the rate of decrement was the same in both conditions. Extra feedback produced the same effect as the shorter work goal. They concluded that the effect of amphetamine was different from motivational effects. A dose of amphetamine had the same effect at whatever stage in the task it was given (Payne, Hauty and Moore, 1957). The effect of the drug was measured by the difference in performance between the last 30 minutes of the practice period and the second hour after the drug was given.

Amphetamine is particularly effective in counteracting the effects of sleep deprivation (Hauty and Payne, 1955, 1958). Kornetsky *et al.*, (1959) found that amphetamine improved performance in a number of tasks when subjects had been kept awake for sixty-eight hours. These tasks included detecting an X or XA in a series of letters, learning connexions between ten lights and response buttons, and a digit-symbol substitution test. The reaction time of fatigued subjects can also be improved by amphetamine (Seashore and Ivy, 1953; Tyler, 1947).

Amphetamine improves performance on the pursuit rotor (Eysenck, Casey and Trouton, 1957) and prevents the reduction in the spiral after-effect found with repeated testing (H. C. Holland, 1963). (See Figure 2, p. 32.)

The effect of amphetamine on vigilance tasks

N. H. Mackworth (1950) found that amphetamine prevented the decrement in detection normally observed in the jump clock test, but did not affect the initial level of performance. Weiner and Ross (1962; Figure 31) examined the effect of amphetamine on the rate of 'observing' responses in a vigilance task. When the subject pressed a lever, he might see either a red light (wanted signal) or a light of another colour (unwanted signal) or nothing, depending on the schedule. The regularity and rate of the unwanted signals was a variable. It was clear from the results that the subject considered these unwanted signals a 'reward' since the observing rate rose with the rate of unwanted signals. There was a significant interaction between the effects of amphetamine and the number of 'unwanted' signals. In general, amphetamine increased the number of observing responses, and this effect was enhanced when there were more unwanted signals. In the condition with no unwanted signals, amphetamine did *not* prevent the decrement in the rate of observing responses that occurred during the session. When 'unwanted' signals were given on a variable schedule averaging one every two seconds, amphetamine *did* prevent the decrement in observing responses that was found with the control condition. The overall effect of amphetamine was greater with the conditions in which the output of observing responses was greatest and showed an increase during the session.

According to the analysis of Jerison, Pickett and Stenson (1965), an increase in observing response should result in an increase in both detections and in false alarms. There is, however, no evidence that amphetamine increases false alarms. J. F. Mackworth (1965) examined the effect of amphetamine

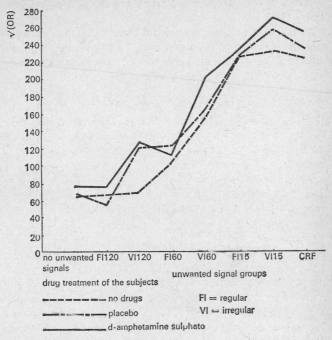

Figure 31 Observer response square roots [√ (OR)] of the unwanted signal groups as a function of the drug treatments of the subjects (from Weiner and Ross, 1962, p. 138)

on detections and false alarms in the continuous clock test. In this test, significant decrements on d′, the detectability of the signal, have been found (see Mackworth, 1970). The drug did not affect the initial level of detection or detectability, but did reduce the decrement in performance and in d′ during the session. There was no significant effect on false alarms. When knowledge of results was given with the drug, the effect was additive. This condition was the only one in which there was a small increase in d′ during the session. In all other conditions, there was a decrease in d′ during the session.

The effects of amphetamine and other drugs on performance in an auditory vigilance task were examined by Loeb,

Hawkes, Evans and Alluisi (1965; Figure 32). The signal was
a slightly louder pulse in a train of pulses occurring every
2·5 seconds. The initial level of detections and detectability
was not affected by amphetamine, but d' was significantly
greater in the third block of trials with amphetamine. False
responses declined during the session under all conditions.
The index of conservatism (beta) increased significantly
under all conditions except with amphetamine. It is possible
that the decline in false alarms is due to a change in expectancy, which might be unaffected by amphetamine.

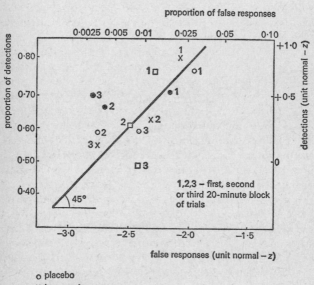

Figure 32 Performance in a one-hour auditory vigilance task
(twenty-four subjects). Receiver operating characteristic (R O C)
curves for each of four drug conditions based on three 20-minute
blocks of time (from Loeb, Hawkes, Evans and Alluisi, 1965,
p. 29)

A study of the effects of amphetamine and benadryl on detections in two kinds of auditory vigilance tasks confirmed the above results (Neal and Pearson, 1966). One task required the detection of three successive odd numbers, and the other, the detection of a longer tone. There were about forty signals per hour. Changes in detection during the session were not significant. The only significant effect on detections was found in the three-way interaction between groups, task and drugs. This was due to the poor performance of females who received benadryl. At the end of the session, the highest level of performance was found with amphetamine and the lowest with benadryl. False alarms were significantly increased with benadryl, while there was no differences in false alarms between the amphetamine and placebo conditions.

An inhibitory effect of amphetamine on performance was found by Uehling and Venator (1967). Rats were required to respond to a slight increase in illumination that came on for 3 seconds at intervals ranging from 1 to 4 minutes. Control subjects detected only about one-third of these signals, and amphetamine decreased detection to a very low level. On the other hand, phenobarbital increased detections. There was no difference between the drugs in the number of bar presses between signals. It was suggested that amphetamine might have a direct inhibitory effect on the visual system.

Amphetamine may have a direct reinforcement effect. Pickens, Meisch and McGuire (1967) found that rats would press a key that gave them an intravenous injection of amphetamine. The rats timed their responses so that they received a fairly stable level of amphetamine for 24–48 hours. The response rate decreased as the drug dosage per injection was increased. After 1 to 2 days of responding, the rats took 12–24 hours off, during which they ate or slept. After 4 weeks of responding, the response pattern deteriorated. The popularity of amphetamine as a drug is all too well known. The popular LSD has also been shown to produce the alert pattern in the EEG, especially when there was adequate sensory stimulation (Elkes, 1961).

It can be concluded that in vigilance tasks, amphetamine

tends to maintain the level of detections without affecting false alarms. In tracking or active scanning tasks, amphetamine may produce an improvement during the session.

Smoking

Nicotine markedly stimulates the central nervous system, though its effect on synapses is first stimulation and then inhibition (Goodman and Gilman, 1958). Smoking may reduce visual sensitivity, peripheral acuity and the efficiency of scanning (Johnston, 1965, 1966; Warwick and Eysenck, 1963). Tarrière and Hartemann (1964) compared the performance of smokers, with and without smoking during the session, with that of non-smokers in a visual vigilance task, which combined detection of peripheral signals with tracking. The results for the signal detection are shown in Figure 33. There was a complete absence of decrement when the smokers were allowed to smoke. In sessions without tobacco, there was

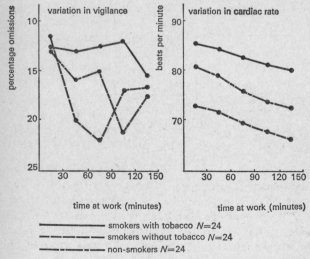

smokers with tobacco N=24
smokers without tobacco N=24
non-smokers N=24

Figure 33 Comparative variation in vigilance and cardiac rate (from Tarrière and Hartemann, 1964, p. 527)

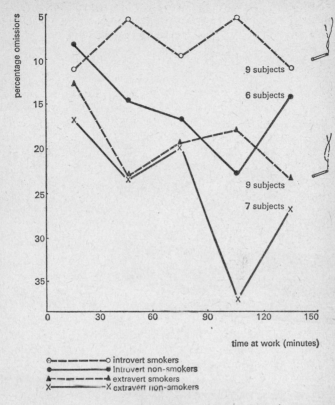

Figure 34 Comparative performances of introverts and extraverts (smokers and non-smokers) (from Tarrière and Hartemann, 1964, p. 528)

a significant decrease in detections during the session for both smokers and non-smokers. There was a drop in cardiac rate during the session with all groups, but the over-all levels of rate were lower with the non-smokers than with the smoking subjects, and lowest in the smokers who were deprived of tobacco.

The subjects were analysed separately on the basis of their

distribution on the extraversion-introversion scale. It was found that the best performance was given by the introvert smokers, while introvert non-smokers performed at about the same level as extravert smokers. Thus, the effects of smoking and introversion appear to be additive. (Figure 34). It was pointed out in chapter 6 that the introvert is supposed to be more aroused than the extravert.

Other Stimulants

Haward (1965) examined the effect of 5-phenyl-2-imino-4-oxo-oxazolidin on a complex mock-up of air traffic control. He found that the drug significantly reduced errors made by highly trained workers, especially in the last half-hour of a two-hour period, when the control subjects showed a significant increase in errors as compared with the initial half-hour. With too high a dose, errors increased.

Conclusions

The marked effect of stimulants upon performance in vigilance tasks is perhaps one of the best arguments in favour of the idea that the decrement is due to a reduction in the level of arousal. The fact that amphetamine does not appear to affect false alarms suggests that the marked decrease in false alarms often found in a vigilance task is due to changes in expectancy, with concurrent reductions in the amplitude of the evoked potential. The fact that the recovery in detections found between sessions is not necessarily accompanied by an equivalent increase in false alarms also suggests that there are two distinct processes.

Tranquillizers and Depressants

In general, the decrement in performance found in vigilance tasks and other continuous tasks is increased by depressant drugs. The reduction in false alarms often found during a vigilance session may be counteracted by depressant or tranquillizing drugs.

The tranquillizer chlorpromazine has been widely studied by physiologists. Kaada and Bruland (1960) summarized the neurological effects of the drug as follows:

1. It depresses the reticular formation, especially the brain stem, leading to increased slow synchronized E E G activity, and
2. It has a powerful inhibitory effect on neurological arousal produced by peripheral stimulation. This is particularly noticeable in the abolition of the orienting response (Tissot and Bovet, 1967).

Elkes (1961) suggested that these drugs in group II (see p. 168) might act by enhancing tonic inhibitory influences from high subcortical regions acting on the reticular core.

The effect of chlorpromazine on habituation of the heart rate response of rates to cold was studied by Glaser (1966); he found that:

1. The response was eliminated by the drug when injected daily before the trial;
2. When in a final trial the injection was omitted, there was still no response, showing that inhibition of the response had not prevented habituation, but on the contrary, had facilitated it;
3. If, however, the drug was injected after normal habituation had occurred over 2 weeks of trials, the response was now as great as the original one, showing that once habituation had been established, the drug abolished it.

Effects of tranquillizers and depressants upon performance

Loeb *et al.*, (1965) found that chlorpromazine and benactyzine produced significant decreases in effective sensitivity during an auditory vigilance task (see Figure 32). Although there was no significant difference between conditions in the decrease of false alarms during the session, the least change was found with chlorpromazine. Similarly, a significantly higher proportion of false alarms was found by Neal and Pearson (1966) when benadryl was given. In both these experiments, the highest level of detections in the last period was found with amphetamine, and the lowest level with the tranquillizer. Bakan (1961) also found a tendency to a greater decrement in detections with meprobamate.

If these drugs are changing the background noise level in the neural system so that variance is least with amphetamine and increases with the tranquillizers, then differences in apparent sensitivity may be expected. Moreover, more observations of non-signal events may reach the criterion level, so that there may be more false alarms with depressants. Wilson (1965) found that chlorpromazine reduced detection of signals by monkeys to a very low level. Kornetsky and Bain (1965) examined the effect of two depressant drugs on the performance of rats in a kind of vigilance task. There were two lights, one of which was non-critical and the other was critical. The critical light lit on an average of once to every six times that the non-critical light appeared. It was found that chlorpromazine reduced the responding rate, without affecting false response, while low doses of pentobarbitol produced a remarkable increase in false responses. The authors suggested that chlorpromazine affects the ability to maintain vigilance while pentobarbitol disrupts the ability to discriminate between stimuli. This description agreed with the findings of Mirsky and Kornetsky (1964) on continuous performance in humans. The complexity of these results emphasizes the differences between depressant drugs. Since the brain consists of a most complex set of subsystems, with inhibition and excitation balanced in harmony, it is to be expected that different drugs will affect now this, now that, aspect of the whole.

Other tasks

Hyoscine and alcohol are also depressants, and have been shown to reduce detections in a proof-reading task (Colquhoun, 1962). Hauty and Payne (1955) reported a more rapid decrement in performance with benadryl on the Multidimensional Pursuit Task. The duration of the spiral after-effect is shortened by meprobamate (Costello, 1960), and with repetitive testing the inhibition of the after-effect develops more rapidly (H. C. Holland, 1963). Amytal reduces the rate of learning the pursuit rotor task (Eysenck, Casey and Trouton, 1957).

The first effect of a sedative may be to reduce the inhibition mediated by the frontal cortex, so that small doses of alcohol, for instance, may produce excitable behaviour similar to that following lobotomy. Neimayer and Siegel (1967) found that activity of rats increased with small doses of phenobarbital, while Uehling and Venator (1967) found better detection of near-threshold signals by rats with small doses of phenobarbital, than with a placebo or amphetamine.

Low oxygen (hypoxia)

Hypoxia resembles in some respects the effects of fatigue. For instance, hypoxia increases the visual threshold (McFarland *et al.*, 1942), increases the number of blocks in the colour-naming task (Bills, 1937) and interacts with fatigue, so that the decrement in this task increases more rapidly with hypoxia. Hypoxia also increases the rate of decrement in the multidimensional tracking task. Hauty, Payne and Bauer (1957) examined the interactions between hypoxia, fatigue and amphetamine. They found that when the tracking task was carried out in 12 per cent oxygen (equivalent to 13,000 feet), there was a greatly increased rate of decrement of performance. After 2 hours, performance was below the level of completely untrained subjects. When given normal (21 per cent) oxygen at this point, performance remained at a constant level, while subjects kept in 12 per cent oxygen continued to decline in performance. Amphetamine completely counteracted the effect of hypoxia for an hour, performance remaining at a constant high level. After this time there was a decline. Performance was, however, at all times at a higher level with those subjects who had received the drug than with the subjects who had not. It would seem that the effect of hypoxia is at least partly to reduce arousal.

This is borne out by the effect of hypoxia upon the EEG (see Lindsley, 1960, p. 1581). Davis, Davis and Thompson (1938) found that when subjects were breathing 8 per cent oxygen, deterioration of writing was noticed as the alpha pattern disappeared, and loss of consciousness was complete when large slow waves of locked pattern appeared. Since the brain is so critically dependent upon a continuous oxidative metabolism (French, 1960), lack of oxygen naturally depresses all functions.

Summary

In general, it would seem probable that the effects of these stimulant and depressant drugs on performance are related to their effects on the background spontaneous activity of the EEG. The effects become most pronounced when the initial arousing effect of the task has become dissipated by continuous attention. Thus, amphetamine may both maintain the background level of alert EEG as well as prevent habituation of the orienting response, while the depressants may have the opposite effect, increasing the rate of habituation and also increasing the amplitude of the spontaneous changes in potential. Amphetamine maintains the level of detections, without increasing false alarms, so that towards the end of the session there are significant differences in sensitivity between the amphetamine subjects and those without this drug. With depressants, there may be a greater decrease in detections and less decrease in false alarms, resulting in a tendency to a lower sensitivity. It would seem that there may be two different processes. Changes in the variance of the background EEG may result in changes in sensitivity; a reduced variance in the alerted condition may lead to an enhanced sensitivity, and increased variance with depressant drugs may lead to reduced sensitivity. On the other hand, the decrease in false alarms normally found in early sessions may be related mainly to a change in expectancy, with perhaps habituation of the evoked responses to the non-signal events of the task. In later sessions such decreases in false alarms are not found (see Mackworth, 1970) and it is likely that habituation of the arousal response becomes more important in such sessions with a well-learned task. In tasks with continuous or very rapid background events the arousal changes may be more important even in early sessions.

9 Summary and Conclusions

The intensive study of any small area of behaviour emphasizes the fact that the brain is an intensely complex pattern of interlocking functions. All of these functions take part to some extent in the smallest act requiring perception, memory and decision. The human brain, we like to believe, is the highest product of evolution. Evolution involves survival of the fittest, and if we enquire, fittest for what, the only answer can be, fittest to survive. That organism which survives long enough to have many offspring will have the greatest effect on the family tree. One of the most important factors in survival is the ability to pay attention to the unidentified and potentially dangerous event, and to ignore the familiar, except when it is known to be important.

One of the first questions that the brain asks of an incoming signal is 'Has this happened before?'. If the answer is 'No', the whole system springs to alert. The source of the strange signal is examined with the greatest care, the head turns, the ears prick, the pupil widens, the ear muscles tense; every random activity in the brain is stilled and an inner silence waits to receive and analyse a second signal. Meanwhile, all the body is prepared for action, the blood flow increases and changes its course, the somatic muscles tense, and the whole organism is ready for fight or flight.

How is that first question answered? How can the organism divide events into new or old, important or unimportant? This basic classification may occur at all neural levels, even in sleep. Clearly, it depends on memory, on a quick flick through a file, and the final answer includes the most detailed analysis of the qualities of the event. *This* faint sound is my child breathing, *that* faint breath is unknown, and instantly

I am alert. There must be precise 'models', 'traces', or records corresponding to a vast number of incoming patterns of neural changes, and a retrieval system so efficient that it can match an event to its record or determine that there is no matching record. All this may occur within a tenth of a second, so that the final neural responses to a particular event are damped or augmented while messages travel throughout the body to bring about a state of alertness, if necessary.

The model contains both spatial and temporal qualities of a repetitive event. When the events occur randomly, habituation is much slower. When two or more kinds of events are expected, the model contains data as to the probable occurrence of each kind. It has been suggested that it is constructed in two stages – a first stage that does not require the cortex, and produces habituation during a session, and a secondary, long-term stage that does involve the cortex and is concerned with habituation between sessions (Nadel, 1966). Other writers, however, consider that the cortex is important in all stages of habituation (see chapter 5). It is possible that vigilance tasks involve only short-term habituation, since habituation between sessions has never been demonstrated in these tasks.

The evolutionary function of this primary classification is to allow maximum attention to the potentially dangerous event. Other events, recognized and classified as unimportant, are dealt with by the routine levels of the brain, and may never reach consciousness at all. We can direct attention to any incoming stimulus we choose, but normally the vast array of messages from the more than ten senses that sample the world for us are largely ignored. As a visual rational animal, man spends most of his life glued to his central vision or to his own thoughts. Other messages are dealt with at a level that never reaches consciousness. Even pain, normally given an over-ride, can be neglected in the heat of battle.

The ruler, the supreme decision maker, the ghost in the machine (Ryle, 1949), is protected by his most efficient cohorts, who allow only the message that they judge to be important to reach him. He reserves his precious and very limited range of vivid central experience for one particular sequence of events out of the multitudes streaming into the central nervous system. Practically all the time the decisions are taken at a lower level, and free will cannot be considered to enter the picture at all. Only when a situation has been presented to the top decision-maker can there be anything other than a purely mechanical, conditioned response.

This filtration is a basic necessity for maximum efficiency in the normal world, but in certain circumstances may not be so efficient. Lulled into a false sense of security by the hypnotic flow of words, the bored auditor may never notice the cunning trap ready to be sprung. Even more bizarre changes may occur. Provided only with repetitive meaningless stimuli that are unable to hold the attention, the brain may provide its own source of entertainment; daydreams or more vivid hallucinations may abstract attention completely from reality. The whole organism is geared to detect change, because change is dangerous, but it is also stimulating. Like other survival needs, food, sleep, sex, even fighting, it has become pleasurable and acts as a primary reward. In a world where multitudes find their other basic needs adequately supplied, the search for novelty and excitement may become a dominant factor. When the external world cannot supply these factors, the search may turn inward towards a maintenance of excitement by drugs.

In the monotonous task, we see the reverse of this. The organism has developed an ability to suppress responses to a repetitive event in order to be able to show maximum sensitivity and responsiveness to a new and unfamiliar event.

The underlying thesis of this book is that the vigilance decrement is a particular example of the process of habituation. Habituation is a response decrement arising as a result of repeated stimulation, and is generally applied to innate or physiological responses (Harris, 1943). It is suggested that: (1) the specific evoked potential and (2) the non-specific neurological arousal response or alpha block produced by the background events are altered as a result of repetition. In tracking tasks in which a positive response is required to every event, it is probable that the same process of habituation is occurring. It cannot, therefore, be considered as negative learning in the sense that the organism is learning that a response is unnecessary. The process probably occurs at an earlier stage on the input side. Habituation may occur at almost any level in the CNS (Thompson and Spencer, 1966); it is likely that in vigilance the most important changes are occurring in the frontal cortex, amygdala, hippocampus and reticular activating system. These changes probably reflect the reduction in the amount of attention paid to the repetitive stimuli. The changes can be regarded as a reduction in either the quality or quantity of *observing responses* made towards the events of the task. Whether they represent solely a reduction in the over-all level of neural response or include diversion of attention to other stimuli is not fully determined.

The importance of the frontal cortex in habituation has been emphasized by Glaser (1966) and Pribram (1967). It has been suggested (Pribram, 1967; Sokolov, 1963) that a model of the repetitive stimuli is formed and from this model expectancies about future events are constructed. If the next stimulus corresponds with the model, in all its parameters, including the time of occurrence, the neural events produced by this stimulus will be inhibited. If the new stimulus does not correspond with the model, then the neural events will pass on unchanged and may even be enhanced, together with inhibition of the spontaneous background rhythms of the brain.

There appears to be another mechanism, which is related to the meaning and importance of the stimulus. This is particularly seen when a stimulus carries the message that it will be followed at a certain time by another one to which response is required. The *contingent negative variation* (Walter *et al.*, 1964), spreading widely through the cortex, probably has the function of sensitizing the cortex to the expected stimulus. It is possible that this process becomes less efficient as the interval between alerting and operant stimulus increases beyond a second. This neural mechanism of expectancy may be one reason why performance in an alerted situation may be superior to that found in the vigilance situation.

The Evoked Potential

There is considerable evidence that the potential evoked by repetitive auditory or visual stimuli habituates, especially in the cortex, both in the specific and the non-specific frontal areas (see chapter 3). Haider, Spong and Lindsley (1964) have shown that there is a correlation between missed signals in a vigilance task and reduced or absent visual potentials evoked by the background events of the task. Changes reported by Wilkinson, Morlock and Williams (1966) are somewhat more difficult to interpret. They found a decrease in the late positive wave and an increase in the late negative wave, which they found to be correlated with missed signals in an auditory vigilance task. This latter change they reported was connected with changes in the level of arousal.

It may be that the reduction in both detections and false alarms, found in the early sessions of many vigilance tasks with repetitive non-signal events, is due to a reduction in the neural responses to these events, although there may also be a real change in criterion If the criterion remains fixed with regard to a certain level of neural event, while the means of both signal and non-signal events are reduced, then the number of both kinds of events that reach this criterial level will be reduced. Consequently, both correct and incorrect positive responses may be reduced. Moreover, the discriminability of the signal may actually be increased when the neural response to the non-signal event is reduced (Weber's Law). This change may counteract any decrease in sensitivity resulting from a change in arousal. It is not possible, at this stage at any rate, to disentangle the effects of expectancy and habituation, especially since they may be two expressions of the same thing. Changes in performance in continuous tasks, however, suggest that the responsivity is not dependent only on the probability that a response will be required. Repetition of a stimulus may lead to habituation even when a positive response is required to every stimulus. Even in these active tasks, the stimulus set is known, however, so that a composite model of probabilities is in existence.

Activation, Arousal and the Orienting Response

The whole body can take part in the orienting response. Its function is to produce maximum readiness to observe and respond to a stimulus, and therefore corresponds with the state of vigilance postulated by Head (1926) and described by Mackworth (1950) as the function investigated by his experiments. The readiness to observe includes external changes of posture, orienting towards the source of the stimulus, changes in sensitivity of the analyzers, changes in the neural patterns and widespread autonomic changes (Duffy, 1962; Sokolov, 1963). Since the orienting response is related to the novelty or unexpectedness of the stimulus, these responses are rapidly reduced as the stimulus is repeated, especially if it is a simple one. Habituation of the orienting reflex probably plays a considerable part in the vigilance decrement, especially at the beginning of a session.

As a result of habituation of the arousal or orienting response, there will be an increase in the spontaneous background neural activity, and a decrease in the sensitivity of the analysers. Hence, there may be a decrease in the detectability of the signal. This has been found in tasks with rapid or continuous event rates (J. F. Mackworth, 1965; 1968 a and b; 1970), while Gunn and Loeb (1967) have suggested that it is related to coupling. It may also be found in circumstances in which the criterion of the subject has stabilized, after many sessions of training (Binford and Loeb, 1966).

It is possible that intersession habituation of the evoked potential may occur more rapidly than intersession habituation of the arousal response. Thus, in later sessions the arousal response might be more important. This might be a partial explanation for (1) the relatively high initial false alarm rate and its rapid decrease within and between sessions, (2) the increased sensitivity sometimes found between sessions and

(3) the decrement in sensitivity found in later sessions.

The relation between habituation of the arousal response and general levels of arousal is complex. There is not necessarily a reduction in the general level of arousal just because habituation of the response to a particular stimulus series has occurred. Nor does a reduction in the general level of arousal necessarily mean a reduction in the arousal response. Habituation of the various measures of arousal may not occur during sleep (Johnson and Lubin, 1967). Periods of drowsiness in a vigilance task may result in renewed responsiveness to the signal and non-signal events when the subject again becomes alert. A number of experiments have suggested that the changes in a vigilance task are related to changes in the over-all level of arousal, which is to be expected in such an unstimulating environment (e.g., Wilkinson *et al.*, 1966). In general, it can be concluded that there are changes in the various measures of arousal during a vigilance task (chapter 6), and most of the data on the different variables that have been examined agree with the hypothesis that there is a decrease in arousal during a monotonous task.

In order to present adequately the evidence relating the vigilance task to habituation of physiological responses, it is necessary to include data which are fully discussed elsewhere (Mackworth, 1970). The following characteristics of habituation are taken from Sokolov (1963), Thompson and Spencer, (1966) and elsewhere (see chapter 5).

1. *Habituation depends on repetition of a stimulus or series of stimuli*, and therefore may occur in any situation in which a limited range of stimuli is presented repetitively. It may affect performance in those situations in which the limitation of performance is set by the readiness to detect and respond to a simple stimulus. It may not occur in situations in which attention can be relaxed and then returned to the task when an alerting stimulus occurs, as in the usual signal detectability tasks. It will also be masked in situations in which performance is limited by skill or mental processes such as coding or memory. Thus, for instance, a complex task in which

the speed of response is reduced by a difficult decision is unlikely to show the effects of habituation. It is possible that when a subject is required to make a decision about the level of confidence at which he is giving his answer, this may alter his performance. Thus, Binford and Loeb (1966) showed that when multiple criteria were required, there was an upswing in detection towards the end of the session. No such upswing was found with a single criterion. Similarly, tasks in which performance is limited by visual scanning, or the probability that a subject will be looking at a particular point when a signal occurs, may also fail to show decrements, as in the three-clock task of Jerison (1963). In these cases there may be an added variety of stimulation introduced by the freedom to alter scanning processes.

The decrement in performance may occur in a fairly complicated tracking task. In this case, it is necessary that the task be well-learned before a decrement is seen. A hidden decrement may, however, be observed by improvement between the end of one trial and the beginning of the next (reminiscence). The similarity of the rate of change in accuracy between vigilance tasks and tracking tasks (see Figure 2, p. 32) suggests a similarity in mechanism. As with habituation, the decrement is approximately exponential. Taylor (1966), summarizing a number of experiments, has pointed out that changes that are related to the square root of time can be found in a wide variety of perceptual tasks. He pointed out that for efficiency, the portion of the perceiving mechanism that is conceded to a redundant input should be reduced, allowing greater capacity for other purposes. This is similar to the idea of a model that inhibits the neural effect of stimuli that coincide with the model. Hebb (1955) suggested that the number of figure reversals seen in a given time might be a measure of arousal. Sherwood (1965) showed that there was a relation between retention of learned material and the number of figure reversals seen. Many of the experiments reported by Taylor concerned transformations of unchanging or repetitive stimuli. Thus it would seem that habituation may include reduction in reactivity to an unchanging but ambiguous stimulus. In many of these perceptual tasks, the changes in response may depend upon construction of a neural model, followed by inhibition of the neural effects of stimuli that correspond with the model.

The tasks discussed above suggest that the decrement is not necessarily dependent upon the probability of a signal. They are characterized by continuous attention to the stimulus situation. When the subject can withdraw his attention from the situation for quite short periods, this may reduce the rate of habituation. His ability to take brief rest-pauses in this way without damaging his performance depends upon his knowledge of the probability of a signal. Thus, if it is clear to him that a signal is unlikely to occur within a given space of time, his performance level may not deteriorate. Such a situation is found in signal detection tasks, and in vigilance tasks in which intersignal interval variability is not great, so that the subject can soon learn the minimum interval. The fact that signals following the minimum interval are often most poorly detected suggests that the subject is taking these intervals for relaxation of attention.

Decrements may be masked by learning. This appears to be particularly likely in auditory tasks (Binford and Loeb, 1966). Broadbent and Gregory (1965) and Colquhoun (1966) both present results indicating improvements in detectability between one session and the next in visual tasks.

In conclusion, decrements are found in well-learned tasks in which performance is limited by the readiness to detect and respond to a simple signal. The tasks require continuous attention to a relatively repetitive situation. The ability to pay attention to a repetitive series of stimuli may decrease as the neural responses to the stimuli decrease, as a result of habituation. These neural responses include both generalized and localized changes in background activity and the specific evoked potentials.

2. *When a stimulus acquires signal status, the orienting reflex is restored* (Sokolov, 1963, p. 163). Rates of decrement in vigilance and other tasks are much slower than habituation

of physiological responses to unimportant stimuli. This is most likely due to the fact that the repetitive stimuli have or may have signal properties. Variations in performance may often be due to the expectancy of the subject as to the probability that a particular event will be a signal. Expectancy may increase arousal (see chapter 4). The rate of decrement of performance should therefore be reduced by increasing the signal rate. This finding has often been reported (e.g. Jenkins, 1958).

3. *The rate of change is a function of the event rate.* Thompson and Spencer (1966) showed that habituation of the flexion reflex was faster when shocks were given at a rate of one per second than when they were given once in 3·2 seconds. Abraham and Marsh (1966) showed that the amplitude of the click response in the auditory cortex was reduced as the stimulus rate increased from one in 10 seconds to four per second. The response in the cochlear nucleus was unaffected by rate (see Figure 5, p. 50). This finding is consistent with the suggestion that habituation of neural response is a cortical function. Webster *et al.*, (1965) showed that there was a rapid initial decrease in amplitude of response in the cochlear nucleus when the rate of stimulus presentation was faster than one per second. No decreases occurred with slower rates of stimulation.

The effect of the *background event rate* on detection in *vigilance tasks* is considerable (see Colquhoun, 1961; Jerison, 1963b; 1968b; Jerison and Pickett, 1964; Loeb and Binford, 1968; Mackworth, 1965; Mackworth, 1970; Weiner and Ross, 1962). When the background event rate is increased, there is a marked reduction in the probability of detection of a signal throughout the task. There may also be an increase in the rate of decrement during the session. It seems likely that the effects of the signal rate and the background event rate are independent.

4. *When discrimination is required, the rate of habituation of the orienting response is reduced when the discrimination is more difficult.* Little research has been carried out on the effect

of signal intensity on vigilance performance. The subject is complex. Different results may be seen when the measure is a change in the percentage of detection than when the measure is the sensitivity (d') or the criterion (beta). Figure 2 suggests that the rate of decrement in continuous tasks is proportional to the initial level, being less when the initial level is low. This figure includes measures of detectability found with a vigilance task, the continuous clock, with two levels of signal amplitude (duration).

5. *Presentation of a different stimulus results in recovery of the habituated response.* Gruber (1964) showed that alternation between visual and auditory modes produced a considerable improvement in vigilance performance. Extra stimuli that do not require discrimination or attention in vigilance tasks fall into two categories, those which give feedback or added motivation (usually acting as reward or punishment), and those which are irrelevant to the main task. Feedback or knowledge of results has been widely found to improve performance in a vigilance task. Irrelevant stimuli may either improve or harm performance, depending on the relative effects of distraction and dishabituation (see chapter 7). There is also the possibility that a state of hyper-arousal may be produced, in which bodily changes may result in decreased performance.

The most beneficial effect of irrelevant stimuli is found with music, jokes or other variable, and perhaps enlivening, auditory material added to a visual task. Even continuous random noise may be beneficial when the subject is sufficiently tired, as when he is suffering from sleep deprivation.

The harmful or distracting effect of loud high-pitched continuous noise may be maximal late in the session with a monotonous task. By then any arousal effect due to novelty has worn off, while the distraction may increase as the novelty of the main stimulus task has also decreased.

6. *Individual differences.* There are marked individual differences in the patterns of habituation of various physiological

responses, and there are also marked differences in the patterns of performance change found in monotonous tasks. It is not, however, certain that people can be distinguished on the basis of an over-all rate of change in all measures of arousal nor of vigilance changes that are independent of the nature of the task. Many experiments have shown correlations between particular physiological measures and performance in a particular task.

Correlations have been found between changes in the evoked potential and the probability of detecting a signal (see chapter 3). Correlations have also been found between performance and various measures of the arousal or orienting response, such as spontaneous galvanic skin responses, changes in adrenalin, skin conductance and the amount of alpha rhythm. Introverts tend to perform better than extraverts in monotonous tasks, and it has been suggested that introverts are more aroused than extraverts in these situations (see chapter 6). Similar individual differences have been described by Russian workers under the names of excitation–inhibition, and weak–strong scales. The lack of consistent changes in all the measures of arousal leaves this formulation somewhat imprecise.

7. *The rate of habituation of the arousal response may be decreased by stimulant drugs, and increased by depressant drugs.* Such stimulant drugs as amphetamine specifically prevent habituation of the neural arousal response. They also prevent the decrement in performance or in detections that occur in monotonous tasks. They do this without affecting false alarms, so that in a task in which false alarms decrease during the control condition, a similar decrease is found with amphetamine. Thus, there is a tendency towards a difference in sensitivity between the drug and control subjects at the end of the session. This difference becomes more marked when amphetamine is compared with sedative or tranquillizer drugs. This finding is the chief basis for the suggestion that decreases in d′ are related to habituation of the arousal response, while increases in beta are related to habituation of the evoked potential. Habituation of the evoked potential may not occur

during sleep; in fact, the amplitude may increase during sleep. Thus, sedative drugs may actually increase the false alarm rate, or at least prevent the usual decrease in false alarms. It has been pointed out that habituation of the evoked potential may theoretically lead to an *increase* in sensitivity, while an increase in the evoked response to the background events may lead to a *decrease* in sensitivity for the small change in these events that constitutes a signal. Such a decrease in sensitivity is found with sedative drugs (Loeb *et al.*, 1965).

8. *Any change in the pattern of the regular repetitive stimulation produces dishabituation.* Even one absent stimulus may evoke an orientation response (Sokolov, 1963, p. 287). If a neuronal model is being compared with actual events, the unexpected absence of a stimulus is just as surprising as an unexpected stimulus. But even an expected rest pause of quite short duration, such as 30 seconds each half-hour, can produce marked improvement in performance. Such rest pauses are often accompanied by novel stimuli, bells or movement, which indicate their occurrence.

Rest pauses of half an hour or longer have generally proved adequate for complete restoration of performance. Such results offer strong support to the concept that habituation of the neural responses to the discrete or continuous background events is the cause of the decrement in performance. There does not seem to be any reason why such brief pauses should produce a change in expectancy or in criterion.

When there is a continuous background movement, as with the continuous clock test, short rest pauses up to ten minutes in duration combined with disappearance of the display, may not improve performance (Mackworth and Taylor, 1963). Even when a new version of the task is introduced every ten minutes, there may not be complete recovery (Mackworth, 1963b). In this task, in which there is a decrement in d′, changes in arousal may be more important than in tasks with discrete background events, in which habituation of the evoked potential may be the important factor. Rest pauses without any physical movement, spent sitting quietly in the same unchanging environment, may provide insufficient novelty to restore the level of arousal or the arousal response.

9. *Sleep loss*. Both the E E G arousal response and the electro-myographic potential response habituate more rapidly when subjects have been deprived of sleep. There is a close relationship between the increasing errors, gaps or omissions found in various tasks performed after loss of sleep, and these physiological measures. False alarms tended to decrease with moderate deprivation of sleep, but to increase again when the sleep deprivation was more severe. Thus, moderate sleep deprivation gives the same effect as prolonged time on task, while more extreme sleep deprivation has the same effect as sedative or tranquillizing drugs.

The effects of sleep loss are counteracted to some extent by knowledge of results and by noise. In general, it appears that subjects suffering from loss of sleep show a more rapid reduction in arousal during a monotonous task than control subjects.

10. *Temperature*. Performance in monotonous tasks may be best at the accustomed environmental temperature, and deteriorate with either higher or lower temperatures. It is possible that bodily discomfort may act as a distraction. The effects of sleep loss and increased temperature may be additive, but there are certain differences between the harmful effects of the two stresses (see chapter 8). The effects of raised temperatures are complex, and it is doubtful whether they can be explained entirely on the basis of arousal. Changes in body temperature will affect all the physiological processes, so that it is not surprising that the effects are complex. Wilkinson *et al.* (1964) found that raised body temperatures improved performance on a vigilance task when the subjects were accustomed to the general situation. On an adding test, however, many more errors were made with the highest temperature.

11. *Complexity of the task*. Tasks which require active head movements for scanning or involve difficult or complex

decisions may show less decrement during the session than tasks which offer single sources and require simple decisions (see Luce, 1964). Thus Jerison (1963) found that when three jump clocks were presented simultaneously there was no decrement from the initial low level of detections. In the second session with two clocks, some decrement appeared. Broadbent (1958) found no increase in reaction time during the session when the signal might appear on any one of twenty dials. Adams and Boulter (1964) found that when they compared spatial and temporal uncertainty, the increase in reaction time during the session was only significant with temporal uncertainty. Hatfield and Loeb (1968) compared three intensities of signal with one intensity, and found that the over-all decrease in detections during the session was less with three intensities. Moreover, there was a decrease in d' with one intensity, but an increase during the session with three. This finding agrees with the suggestions that increased complexity prevents the decrement in arousal, and that decrements in d' are related to a decrement in arousal.

Response complexity is also important. Adams, Stenson and Humes (1961) found that with a simple response there was an increase in latency during the session, but no intra-session increase in latency was found when a complex evaluation was required. Binford and Loeb (1966) compared the effects of requiring single or multiple criteria, and found that there was an end-spurt, an improvement in detections towards the end of the session, with the multiple criteria, but not with the single criterion. Values for d' were also higher with the multiple criteria. Broadbent and Gregory (1963b, 1965) and Levine (1966) found no decrements in d' in tasks where multiple criteria were employed. Increases in beta were found in these tasks. It has been suggested that decrements in d' may be related to a reduction in the arousal response, while increases in beta may be related to habituation of the evoked potential.

General Conclusions

While there is a good deal of evidence that there is a decrease in arousal during a monotonous task, and some evidence that this decrease is correlated with the decrement in performance, it cannot be said that the hypothesis is proved. This conclusion is even more applicable to changes in the evoked potential, which at present have been examined in two experiments with regard to signal detection, and a few more with regard to the changes in latency. It is hoped that this summary of the available material will suggest the necessary experiments, with the important controls.

It is not possible to separate the various hypotheses that have been put forward to account for the vigilance decrement. The subject's estimate of the probability that an event will be a signal will affect his observing responses, the amplitude of the evoked potential, the level of the arousal response, and the degree of inhibition of physiological responses, as well as the probability that he will answer yes or no to a particular level of observed event. Thus, it would seem that at this time it is better to determine as widely as possible the various concomitant changes in the physiological and psychological responses of the subject, rather than trying to distinguish between one theory and another.

With this warning, a final restatement of the suggested chain of events will be given. It would appear that two relatively independent processes must be postulated in order to explain the data. These processes are thought to be habituation of the responses evoked by the events of the task, and habituation of the arousal response; the arousal response involves a decrease in the amplitude of the spontaneous neural rhythms, so that the incoming neural response becomes more clearly defined. There may also be a decrease in the general level of arousal, resulting from the relatively unchanging nature of the general environment, leading to moments of drowsiness. Such moments of rest may result in dishabituation of the evoked response, and restoration of the level of performance. It is proposed that as a result of habituation of the evoked responses to the repetitive events of the task, fewer of these evoked responses will reach the previously established criterial level. Thus, there may be a decrease in both correct detections and false alarms in a vigilance task, resulting in an apparent increase in criterial level. The ability to distinguish the signal from the non-signal event may actually be improved by reductions in the amplitude of the evoked responses to the non-signal events. An increase in the spontaneous neural noise, due to a reduction in the arousal response, and in the general level of arousal, may however decrease sensitivity. Thus when both the evoked potentials and the arousal responses are decreasing together, there may be no apparent change in d'. In later sessions, changes in the arousal response may become more important than changes in the evoked responses.

The brain appears to be a machine programmed to clear from the decision-making centre all redundant information. It leaves this protective function to a level that is not very selective. The boy who cries 'wolf' too often receives no attention when finally his warning is real. Seen at its simplest level in the vigilance task, this built-in mechanism can act at all levels of complexity. It can become highly dangerous at levels involving the survival of the individual, as in driving, or the survival of the species. It is certain that if we ever delegate our decision-making function to machines, we shall be in deep trouble. The vigilance task is aptly named. It deals with the same faculty as that involved in the statement 'The price of liberty is eternal vigilance.'

References

ABRAHAM, F. D., and MARSH, J. T. (1966), 'Amplitude of evoked potentials as a function of slow presenting rates of repetitive auditory stimulation', *Exp. Neurology*, vol. 14, pp. 187–98.

ABRAHAMS, V. C., and LANGWORTH, E. P. (1967), 'The contribution of background electrical activity to the form of averaged evoked potentials in chloralose anaesthetized cats', *Exp. Neurology*, vol. 18, pp. 253–66.

ADAMS, J. A. (1955), 'A source of decrement in psychomotor performance', *J. exp. Psychol.*, vol. 49, pp. 390–94.

ADAMS, J. A., STENSON, H. H., and HUMES, J. M. (1961), 'Monitoring of complex visual displays: effects of visual load and response complexity on human vigilance', *Human Factors*, vol. 3, pp. 312–21.

ANDERSON, I. H., *et al.* (1944), 'Radar operator fatigue: the effects of length and repetition of operating periods on efficiency of performance', *O.S.R.D. Report* no. 3334, *Res. Report* no. 6.

ANDREASSI, J. L. (1966a), 'Effects of regular and irregular signal patterns upon skin conductance and reaction time', *Percept. mot. Skills*, vol. 23, pp. 975–8.

ANDREASSI, J. L. (1966b), 'Skin conductance and reaction-time in a continuous auditory monitoring task', *Am. J. Psychol.*, vol. 79, pp. 470–74.

ARMINGTON, J. C., and MITNICK, L. L. (1959), 'Electroencephalogram and sleep deprivation', *J. appl. Physiol.*, vol. 14, pp. 247–50.

AX, A., and LUBY, E. D. (1961), 'Autonomic responses to sleep deprivation', *A.M.A. Arch. gen. Psychiatry*, vol. 4, pp. 55–9.

BAGSHAW, M. H., KIMBLE, D. P., and PRIBRAM, K. H. (1965), 'The GSR of monkeys during orienting and habituation and after ablation of the amygdala, hippocampus, and inferotemporal cortex', *Neuropsychologia*, vol. 3, pp. 111–19.

BAKAN, P. (1955), 'Discrimination decrement as a function of time on a prolonged vigil', *J. exp. Psychol.*, vol. 50, pp. 387–9.

BAKAN, P. (1959), 'Extraversion, introversion and improvement in an auditory vigilance task', *Brit. J. Psychol.*, vol. 50, pp. 325–32.

BAKAN, P. (1961), 'Effect of meprobamate on auditory vigilance', *Percept. mot. Skills*, vol. 12, p. 26.

BAKAN, P. (1963a), 'An analysis of retrospective reports following an auditory vigilance task', in D. N. Buckner and J. J. McGrath (eds.), *Vigilance: A Symposium*, McGraw-Hill, pp. 88–100.

BAKAN, P. (1963b), 'Time-of-day preference, vigilance, and extra-version-introversion', in D. N. Buckner and J. J. McGrath (eds.), *Vigilance: A Symposium*, McGraw-Hill, pp. 114–16.

BAKAN, P., BELTON, J. A., and TOTH, J. C. (1963), 'Extraversion-introversion and decrement in an auditory vigilance task', in D. N. Buckner and J. J. McGrath (eds.), *Vigilance: A Symposium*, McGraw-Hill, pp. 22–8.

BAKER, C. H. (1963a), 'Further towards a theory of vigilance', in D. N. Buckner and J. J. McGrath (eds.), *Vigilance: A Symposium*, McGraw-Hill, pp. 127–53.

BAKER, C. H. (1963b), 'Consistency of performance in two visual vigilance tasks', in D. N. Buckner and J. J. McGrath (eds.), *Vigilance: A Symposium*, McGraw-Hill, pp. 43–50.

BAKER, R. A., and WARE, J. R. (1966), 'The relationship between vigilance and monotonous work', *Ergonomics*, vol. 9, pp. 109–14.

BAKER, R. A., WARE, J. R., and SIPOWICZ, R. R. (1962), 'Signal detection by multiple monitors', *Psychol. Record*, vol. 12, pp. 133–7.

BARNES, C. D. (1966), 'The interaction of amphetamine and eserine on the EEG', *Life Sciences*, vol. 5, pp. 1891–902.

BAUST, W., and NIEMCZYK, H. (1964), 'Further studies on the action of adrenergic drugs on cortical activity', *Electroenceph. clin. Neurophysiol.*, vol. 17, pp. 261–71.

BELL, C. R., PROVINS, K. A., and HIORNS, R. W. (1964), 'Visual and auditory vigilance during exposure to hot and humid conditions', *Ergonomics*, vol. 7, pp. 279–88.

BERGER, C., and MAHNEKE, A. (1954), 'Fatigue in two simple visual tasks', *Am. J. Psychol.*, vol. 67, pp. 509–12.

BERLYNE, D. E. (1960), *Conflict, Arousal and Curiosity*, McGraw-Hill.

BERLYNE, D. E. (1966), 'Curiosity and exploration', *Science*, vol. 153, pp. 25–33.

BERLYNE, D. E., and McDONELL, P. (1965), 'Effects of stimulus complexity and incongruity on duration of EEG desynchronization', *Electroenceph. clin. Neurophysiol.*, vol. 18, pp. 156–61.

BERLYNE, D. E., and NICKI, R. M. (1966), 'Effects of the pitch and duration of tones on EEG desynchronization', *Psychon. Sci.*, vol. 4, pp. 101–2.

BERLYNE, D. E., and PECKHAM, S. (1966), 'The semantic differential and other measures of reaction to visual complexity', *Canad. J. Psychol.*, vol. 20, pp. 125–35.

BERTELSON, P., and JOFFE, R. (1963), 'Blockings in prolonged seria responding', *Ergonomics*, vol. 5, pp. 109–16.

BILLS, A. G. (1931), 'Blocking: a new principle in mental fatigue', *Am. J. Psychol.*, vol. 43, pp. 230–45.

BILLS, A. G. (1937), 'Blocking in mental fatigue and anoxemia compared', *J. exp. Psychol.*, vol. 20, pp. 437–52.

BINFORD, J. R., and LOEB, M. (1966), 'Changes within and over repeated sessions in criterion and effective sensitivity in an auditory vigilance task', *J. exp. Psychol.*, vol. 72, pp. 339–45.

BJERNER, B. (1949), 'Alpha depression and lowered pulse rate during delayed actions in a serial reaction test', *Acta physiol. Scand.*, vol. 19, supp. 65.

BOGACZ, J., VANZULLI, A., and GARCÍA-AUSTT, E. (1962), 'Evoked responses in man. IV. Effects of habituation, distraction and conditioning upon auditory evoked responses', *Acta neurol. Lat. Amer.*, vol. 8, pp. 244–52.

BRAZIER, M. (1964), 'Evoked responses recorded from the depths of the human brain', in H. E. Whipple (ed.), *Sensory Evoked Response in Man*, Annals N.Y. Acad. Sciences, vol. 112, pp. 33–59.

BROADBENT, D. E. (1953), 'Noise, paced performance, and vigilance tasks', *Brit. J. Psychol.*, vol. 44, pp. 428–33.

BROADBENT, D. E. (1958), *Perception and Communication*, Pergamon Press.

BROADBENT, D. E., and GREGORY, M. (1963a), 'Division of attention and the decision theory of signal detection', *Proc. Roy. Soc. B.*, vol. 158, pp. 222–31.

BROADBENT, D. E., and GREGORY, M. (1963b), 'Vigilance considered as a statistical decision', *Brit. J. Psychol.*, vol. 54, pp. 309–23.

BROADBENT, D. E., and GREGORY, M. (1965), 'Effects of noise and of signal rate upon vigilance analysed by means of decision theory', *Human Factors*, vol. 7, pp. 155–62.

BROWN, I. D., TICKNER, A. H., and SIMMONDS, D. C. V. (1966), 'Effects of prolonged driving upon driving skill and performance of a subsidiary task', *Industrial Med. Surgery*, vol. 35, pp. 760–65.

BUCK, L. (1966), 'Reaction time as a measure of perceptual vigilance', *Psychol. Bull.*, vol. 65, pp. 291–304.

BUCKNER, D. N. (1963), 'An individual-difference approach to explaining vigilance performance', in D. N. Buckner and J. J. McGrath (eds.), *Vigilance: A Symposium*, McGraw-Hill, pp. 171–9.

BUCKNER, D. N., HARABEDIAN, A., and MCGRATH, J. J. (1960), 'A study of individual differences in vigilance performance', *Technical Rpt*, no. 2, Human Factors Research, Los Angeles.

BUCKNER, D. N., HARABEDIAN, A., and MCGRATH, J. J. (1965), 'Individual differences in vigilance performance', *J. eng. Psychol.*, vol. 4, pp. 69–85.

BUCKNER, D. N., and MCGRATH, J. J. (eds.) (1963), *Vigilance: A Symposium*, McGraw-Hill.

CANNON, W. B. (1936), *Bodily Changes in Pain, Hunger, Fear and Rage*, Appleton-Century-Crofts.

CATALANO, J. F. (1967), 'Arousal as a factor in reminiscence', *Percept. mot. Skills*, vol. 24, pp. 1171–80.

CATALANO, J. F., and WHALEN, P. M. (1967a), 'Factors in recovery from performance decrement: activation, inhibition and warm-up', *Percept. mot. Skills*, vol. 24, pp. 1223–31.

CATALANO, H. F., and WHALEN, P. M. (1967b), 'Effects of auditory stimulation upon decrement and reminiscence in rotary pursuit tracking', *Percept. mot. Skills*, vol. 25, pp. 981–9.

CHAPANIS, A. (1964), 'Knowledge of results as an incentive in repetitive, monotonous tasks', *J. appl. Psychol.*, vol. 48, pp. 263–7.

CLARIDGE, G. S. (1960), 'The excitation-inhibition balance in neurotics', in H. J. Eysenck (ed.), *Experiments in Personality*, vol. 2, Praeger.

COLQUHOUN, W. P. (1960), 'Temperament, inspection efficiency and time of day', *Ergonomics*, vol. 3, pp. 377–8.

COLQUHOUN, W. P. (1961), 'The effect of "unwanted" signals on performance in a vigilance task', *Ergonomics*, vol. 4, pp. 41–51.

COLQUHOUN, W. P. (1962), 'Effects of hyoscine and meclozine on vigilance and short-term memory', *Brit. J. industr. Med.*, vol. 19, pp. 287–98.

COLQUHOUN, W. P. (1966), 'Training for vigilance: a comparison of different techniques', *Human Factors*, vol. 8, pp. 7–12.

COLQUHOUN, W. P., and BADDELEY, A. D. (1964), 'Role of pretest expectancy in vigilance decrement', *J. exp. Psychol.*, vol. 68, pp. 156–60.

COLQUHOUN, W. P., and BADDELEY, A. D. (1967), 'The influence of signal probability during pretraining on vigilance decrement', *J. exp. Psychol.*, vol. 73, pp. 153–4.

COLQUHOUN, W. P., and CORCORAN, D. W. J. (1964), 'The effects of time of day and social isolation on the relationship between temperament and performance', *Brit. J. soc. clin. Psychol.*, vol. 3, pp. 226–31.

CORCORAN, D. W. J. (1962), 'Noise and loss of sleep', *Quart. J. exp. Psychol.*, vol. 14, pp. 178–82.

CORCORAN, D. W. J. (1963), 'Doubling the rate of signal presentation in a vigilance task during sleep deprivation', *J. appl. Psychol.*, vol. 47, pp. 412–15.

CORCORAN, D. W. J. (1964), 'Changes in heart rate and performance as a result of loss of sleep', *Brit. J. Psychol.*, vol. 55, pp. 307–14.

CORCORAN, D. W. J. (1965), 'Personality and the inverted-U relation', *Brit. J. Psychol.*, vol. 56, pp. 267–73.

CORMAN, C. D. (1967), 'Stimulus generalization of habituation of the galvanic skin response', *J. exp. Psychol.*, vol. 74, pp. 236–40.

COSTELLO, C. G. (1960), 'The effect of meprobamate on perception', *J. ment. Sci.*, vol. 106, pp. 322–5.

COULES, J. C., and AVERY, D. L. (1966), 'Human performance and basal skin conductance in a vigilance-type task with and without knowledge of results', *Percept. mot. Skills*, vol. 23, pp. 1295–302.

DANIEL, R. S. (1967), 'Alpha and theta E E G in vigilance', *Percept. mot. Skills*, vol. 25, pp. 697–703.

DARDANO, J. F. (1962), 'Relationship of intermittent noise, inter-signal interval, and skin conductance to viligance behavior', *J. appl. Psychol.*, vol. 46, pp. 106–14.

DAVIES, D. R., and HOCKEY, G. R. J. (1966), 'The effects of noise and doubling the signal frequency on individual differences in visual vigilance performance', *Brit. J. Psychol.*, vol. 57, pp. 381–9.

DAVIES, D. R., and KRKOVIC, A. (1965), 'Skin-conductance, alpha-activity and vigilance', *Am. J. Psychol.*, vol. 78, pp. 304–6.

DAVIS, H. (1964), 'Enhancement of evoked cortical potentials in humans related to a task requiring a decision', *Science*, vol. 145, pp. 182–3.

DAVIS, P. A., DAVIS, H., and THOMPSON, J. W. (1938), 'Progressive changes in the human electroencephalogram under low oxygen tension', *Am. J. Physiol.*, vol. 123, pp. 51–2.

DEESE, J. (1955), 'Some problems in the theory of vigilance', *Psychol. Rev.*, vol. 62, pp. 359–68.

DELORGE, J. O., HESS, J., and CLARK, F. C. (1967), 'Observing behavior in the squirrel monkey in a situation analogous to human monitoring', *Percept. mot. Skills*, vol. 25, pp. 745–67.

DIAMOND, S. P. (1964), 'Input-output relations', in H. E. Whipple (ed.), *Sensory Evoked Response in Man*, Annals N.Y. Acad. Sciences, pp. 160–71.

DITCHBURN, R.W. (1943), *Some Factors Affecting Efficiency of Work of Lookouts*, Admiralty Research Laboratory Report, /ARL/RI/84/46/0.

DOANE, B. K., MAHATOO, W., HERON, W., and SCOTT, T. H. (1959), 'Changes in perceptual function after isolation', *Canad. J. Psychol.*, vol. 13, pp. 210–19.

DOMINO, E. F., and CORSSEN, G. (1964), 'Visually evoked response in anaesthetized man with and without induced muscle paralysis', in H. E. Whipple (ed.), *Sensory Evoked Response in Man*, Annals N.Y. Acad. Sciences, pp. 226–37.

DONCHIN, E., and COHEN, L. (1967), 'Averaged evoked potentials and intramodality selective attention', *Electroenceph. clin. Neurophysiol.*, vol. 22, pp. 537–46.

DONCHIN, E., and LINDSLEY, D. B. (1965), 'Visually evoked response correlates of perceptual masking and enhancement', *Electroenceph. clin. Neurophysiol.*, vol. 19, pp. 325–35.

DONCHIN, E., and LINDSLEY, D. B. (1966), 'Averaged evoked potential and reaction time to visual stimuli', *Electroenceph. clin. Neurophysiol.*, vol. 20, pp. 217–23.

DOUGLAS, R. J. (1967), 'The hippocampus and behavior', *Psychol. Bull.*, vol. 67, pp. 416–42.

DOUGLAS, R. J., and PRIBRAM, K. H. (1966), 'Learning and limbic lesions', *Neuropsychol.*, vol. 4, pp. 197–220.

DUFFY, E. (1934), 'Emotion: an example of the need for reorientation in psychology', *Psychol. Rev.*, vol. 41, pp. 184–98.

DUFFY, E. (1957), 'The psychological significance of the concept of "arousal" or "activation"', *Psychol. Rev.*, vol. 64, pp. 265–75.

DUFFY, E. (1962), *Activation and Behavior*, Wiley.

DUNLOP, C. W., WEBSTER, W. R., and RODGER, R. S. (1966), 'Amplitude changes of evoked potentials in the auditory system of unanaesthetized cats during acoustic habituation', *J. aud. Res.*, vol. 6, pp. 47–66.

EASON, R., BEARDSHALL, A., and JAFFEE, S. (1965), 'Performance and physiological indicants of activation in a vigilance situation', *Percept. mot. Skills*, vol. 20, pp. 3–13.

EASON, R. G., ODEN, D., and WHITE, C. T. (1967), 'Visually evoked cortical potentials and reaction time in relation to site of retinal stimulation', *Electroenceph. clin. Neurophysiol.*, vol. 23, pp. 213–24.

EIJKMAN, E., and VENDRIK, A. J. H. (1965), 'Can a sensory system be specified by its internal noise?', *J. acoust. Soc. Am.*, vol. 37, pp. 1102–9.

ELKES, J. (1961), 'Drugs influencing affect and behavior: possible neural correlates in relation to mode of action', in A. S. Simon (ed.), *The Physiology of Emotions*, Charles C. Thomas, pp. 95–149.

ELLIOTT, E. (1957), 'Auditory vigilance tasks', *Advancement of Science*, no. 53, pp. 393–9.

EYSENCK, H. J. (ed.) (1963), *Experiments with Drugs*, Macmillan.

EYSENCK, H. J., CASEY, S., and TROUTON, D. S. (1957), 'Drugs and personality, II. The effect of stimulant and depressant drugs on continuous work', *J. ment. Sci.*, vol. 103, pp. 645–9.

EYSENCK, H. J., and THOMPSON, W. (1966), 'The effect of distraction on pursuit rotor learning performance and reminiscence', *Brit. J. Psychol.*, vol. 57, pp. 99–106.

FERNANDEZ-GUARDIOLA, A., ROLDÁN, E., FANJUL, L., and CASTELLS, C. (1961), 'Role of the pupillary mechanism in the process of habituation of the visual pathways', *Electroenceph. clin. Neurophysiol.*, vol. 13, pp. 564–76.

FISKE, D. W., and MADDI, S. R. (1961), *Functions of Varied Experience*, The Dorsey Press.

FOX, S. (1964), 'Evoked potential habituation and sensory pattern preference as determined by stimulus information', *J. comp. physiol. Psychol.*, vol. 58, pp. 257–72.

FRANKMANN, J. P., and ADAMS, J. A. (1962), 'Theories of vigilance', *Psychol. Bull.*, vol. 59, pp. 257–72.

FREEDMAN, N. L., HAFER, B. M., and DANIEL, R. S. (1966), 'EEG arousal decrement during paired-associate learning', *J. comp. physiol. Psychol.*, vol. 61, pp. 15–19.

FREEMAN, G. L. (1940), 'The relation between performance and bodily activity level', *J. exp. Psychol.*, vol. 26, pp. 602–8.

FRENCH, J. D. (1960), 'The reticular formation', in J. Field (ed.), *Handbook of Physiology*, Am. Physiol. Soc., vol. 2, ch. 52.

FRIEL, C. M., and DEROGATIS, L. (1965), 'The effect of non-patterned deprivation on visual recognition thresholds', *Psychon. Sci.*, vol. 3, pp. 163–4.

FROHMAN, E., and LUBY, E. D. (1964), 'Some biochemical findings in sleep deprivation', *Symposium on Medical Aspects of Stress in the Military Climate*, Walter Reed Army Institute of Research, pp. 203–9.

GAARDER, K., KRAUSKOPF, J., GRAF, V., KROPFL, W., and ARMINGTON, J. C. (1964), 'Averaged brain activity following saccadic eye movements', *Science*, vol. 146, pp. 1481–3.

GALAMBOS, R., SHEATZ, G., and VERNIER, V. G. (1956), 'Electrophysiological correlates of a conditioned response in cats', *Science*, vol. 123, pp. 376–7.

GARCÍA-AUSTT, E. (1963), 'Influence of the states of awareness upon sensory evoked potentials', in R. Hernández-Peón (ed.), *The Physiological Basis of Mental Activity*, *Electroenceph. clin. Neurophysiol.*, suppl. 24, pp. 76–89.

GARCÍA-AUSTT, E., BOGACZ, J., and VANZULLI, A. (1961), 'Changes in EEG background activity during photic habituation in man', *Acta neurol. Lat. Amer.*, vol. 7, pp. 82–90.

GARCÍA-AUSTT, E., BOGACZ, J., and VANZULLI, A. (1964), 'Effects of attention and inattention upon visual evoked response', *Electroenceph. clin. Neurophysiol.*, vol. 17, pp. 136–43.

GETTYS, C. (1964), 'The alerted effective threshold in an auditory vigilance task', *J. aud. Res.*, vol. 4, pp. 23–38.

GLASER, E. M. (1966), *The Physiological Basis of Habituation*, Oxford University Press.

GOODMAN, L. S., and GILMAN, A. (1958), *The Pharmacological Basis of Therapeutics*, Macmillan.

GRAY, J. A. (1967), 'Strength of the nervous system: introversion-extraversion, conditionability and arousal', *Behav. Res. Ther.*, vol. 5, pp. 151–69.

GREEN, D. M., and SWETS, J. (1966), *Signal Detection Theory and Psychophysics*, Wiley.

GRUBER, A. (1964), 'Sensory alternation and performance in a vigilance task' *Human Factors*, vol. 6, pp. 3–12.

GRUENINGER, W. E., KIMBLE, D. P., GRUENINGER, J., and LEVINE, S. (1965), 'GSR and corticosteroid response in monkeys with frontal ablations', *Neuropsychologia*, vol. 3, pp. 205–16.

GUNN, W. J., and LOEB, M. (1967), 'Correlation of performance in detecting visual and auditory signals', *Am. J. Psychol.*, vol. 80, pp. 236–42.

HAIDER, M., and DIXON, N. F., (1961), 'Influence of training and fatigue on the continuous recording of a visual differential threshold' *Brit. J. Psychol.*, vol. 52, pp. 227–37.

HAIDER, M., SPONG, P., and LINDSLEY, D. B. (1964), 'Attention, vigilance and cortical evoked potential in humans', *Science*, vol. 145, pp. 180–81.

HALCOMB, C. G., and KIRK, R. E. (1965), 'Organismic variables as predictors of vigilance behavior', *Percept. mot. Skills*, vol. 21, pp. 547–52.

HARRIS, J. D. (1943), 'Habituation response decrement in the intact organism', *Psychol. Bull.*, vol. 40, pp. 385–422.

HATFIELD, J. L., and LOEB, M. (1968), 'Sense mode and coupling in a vigilance task', *Percept. Psychophysics*, vol. 4, pp. 29–36.

HAUTY, G. T., and PAYNE, R. B. (1955), 'Mitigation of work decrement', *J. exp. Psychol.*, vol. 49, pp. 60–67.

HAUTY, G. T., and PAYNE, R. B. (1958), 'Effects of analeptic and depressant drugs upon physiological behavior', *Am. J. pub. Health*, vol. 48, pp. 571–7.

HAUTY, G. T., PAYNE, R. B., and BAUER, R. O. (1957), 'Effects of normal air and dextro-amphetamine upon work decrement induced by oxygen impoverishment and fatigue', *J. Pharmacol.*, vol. 119, pp. 385–9.

HAWARD, L. R. C. (1965), 'Drug-induced fatigue in air-traffic control', *Percept. mot. Skills*, vol. 20, p. 952.

HEAD, H. (1926), *Aphasia*, Cambridge University Press.

HEARST, E., and WHALEN, R. E. (1963), 'Facilitating effects of d-amphetamine on discriminated-avoidance performance', *J. comp. physiol. Psychol.*, vol. 56, pp. 124–8.

HEBB, D. O. (1955), 'Drives and the c.n.s. (conceptual nervous system)', *Pyschol. Rev.*, vol. 62, pp. 243–54. Reprinted in K. H. Pribram (ed.), *Brain and Behaviour 4: Adaptation*, Penguin Books, 1969, pp. 173–90.

HENRY, C. E., and OBRIST, W. (1958), 'The effect of meprobamate on the EEG', *J. nerv. ment. Dis.*, vol. 126, pp. 268–71.

HERBERT, M. J., and JAYNES, W. E. (1964), 'Performance decrement in vehicle driving', *J. engin. Psychol.*, vol. 3, pp. 1–8.

HERNÁNDEZ-PEÓN, R. (1960), 'Neurophysiological correlates of habituation and other manifestations of plastic inhibition', in H. H. Jasper and G. D. Smirnow (eds.), *The Moscow Colloquium on Electroencephalography of Higher Nervous Activity*, *Electroenceph. clin. Neurophysiol.*, suppl. 13, pp. 101–14.

HERNÁNDEZ-PEÓN, R., JOUVET, M., and SCHERRER, H. (1957), 'Auditory potentials at cochlear nucleus during acoustic habituation', *Acta neurol. Lat. Amer.*, vol. 3, pp. 144–56.

HERNÁNDEZ-PEÓN, R., and SCHERRER, H. (1955), '"Habituation" to acoustic stimuli in cochlear nucleus', *Fed. Proc.*, vol. 14, p. 71.

HERNÁNDEZ-PEÓN, R., and STERMAN, M. B. (1966), 'Brain functions', *Ann. Rev. Psychol.*, vol. 17, pp. 363–94.

HERON, A. A. (1956), 'Two-part personality measure for use as a research criterion', *Brit. J. Psychol.*, vol. 47, pp. 243–51.

HESS, E. H., and POLT, J. M. (1960), 'Pupil size as related to interest value of visual stimuli', *Science*, vol. 132, pp. 349–50.

HESS, E. H., and POLT, J. M. (1964), 'Pupil size in relation to mental activity during simple problem solving', *Science*, vol. 143, pp. 1190–92.

HESS, E. H., and POLT, J. M. (1966), 'Changes in pupil size as a measure of taste difference', *Percept. mot. Skills*, vol. 23, pp. 451–5.

HESS, W. R. (1944), 'Das schlafsyndrom als folge dienzephaler reizung', *Helv. Physiol. Acta*, vol. 2, pp. 305–44.

HILLYARD, S. A., and GALAMBOS, R. (1967), 'Effects of stimulus and response contingencies on a surface negative slow potential shift in man', *Electroenceph. clin. Neurophysiol.*, vol. 22, pp. 297–304.

HOLLAND, H. C. (1963), 'Massed practice and reactive inhibition, reminiscence and disinhibition in the spiral after-effect', *Brit. J. Psychol.*, vol. 54, pp. 261–72.

HOLLAND, J. G. (1958), 'Human vigilance', *Science*, vol. 128, pp. 61–7. Reprinted in D. N. Buckner and J. J. McGrath (eds.), *Vigilance: A Symposium*, McGraw-Hill, 1963.

HUMPHREY, G. (1930), 'Extinction and negative adaptation', *Psychol. Rev.*, vol. 37, pp. 361–3.

IRWIN, D. A., KNOTT, J. R., MCADAM, D. W., and REBERT, C. S. (1966), 'Motivational determinants of the "Contingent Negative Variation"', *Electroenceph. clin. Neurophysiol.*, vol. 21, pp. 538–43.

JENKINS, H. M. (1958), 'The effect of signal rate on performance in visual monitoring', *Am. J. Psychol.*, vol. 71, pp. 647–61.

JERISON, H. J. (1957), 'Performance on a simple vigilance task in noise and quiet', *J. acoust. Soc. Am.*, vol. 29, pp. 1163–5.

JERISON, H. J. (1963), 'On the decrement function in human vigilance', in D. N. Buckner and J. J. McGrath (eds.), *Vigilance: A Symposium*, McGraw-Hill, pp. 199–212.

JERISON, H. J. (1965), 'Human and animal vigilance', *Percept. mot. Skills*, vol. 21, pp. 580–82.

JERISON, H. J. (1967a), 'Signal detection theory in the analysis of human vigilance', *Human Factors*, vol. 9, pp. 285–8.

JERISON, H. J. (1967b), 'Activation and long term performance', in A. F. Sanders (ed.), *Attention and Performance*. Reprinted in *Acta Psychologica*, vol. 27, pp. 373–89.

JERISON, H. J., and PICKETT, R. M. (1963), '"Vigilance": a review re-evaluation', *Human Factors*, vol. 5, pp. 211–38.

JERISON, H. J., and PICKETT, R. M. (1964), '"Vigilance": the importance of the elicited observing rate', *Science*, vol. 143, pp. 970–71.

JERISON, H. J., PICKETT, R. M., and STENSON, H. H. (1965), 'The elicited observing rate and decision processes in vigilance', *Human Factors*, vol. 7, pp. 107–28.

JOHN, E. R. (1967), *Mechanisms of Memory*, Academic Press.

JOHNSON, L. C. (1963), 'Some attributes of spontaneous autonomic activity', *J. comp. physiol Psychol.*, vol. 56, pp. 415–22.

JOHNSON, L. C., and LUBIN, A. (1967), 'The orienting reflex during waking and sleeping', *Electroenceph. clin. Neurophysiol.*, vol. 22, pp. 11–21.

JOHNSTON, D. M. (1965), 'A preliminary report on the effect of smoking on size of visual fields', *Life Sciences*, vol. 4, pp. 2215–21.

JOHNSTON, D. M. (1966), 'The effect of smoking on visual search performance', *Percept. mot. Skills*, vol. 22, pp. 619–22.

JONES, B. F., FLINN, R. H., and HAMMOND, E. C. (1941), 'Fatigue and hours of service of interstate truck drivers', *Publ. Health Bull.*, no. 265, Washington D.C. Govt Printing Office.

JUNG, C. G. (1923), *Psychological Types, or the Psychological Individuation*, translated by H. G. Baynes, Pantheon Books, 1959. See also V. S. de Laszlo (ed.), *The Basic Writings of C. G. Jung*, Random House, 1959.

KAADA, B. R., and BRULAND, H. (1960), 'Blocking of the cortically induced behavioral attention (orienting) response by chlorpromazine', *Psychopharm.*, vol. 1, pp. 372–88.

KAHNEMAN, D., and BEATTY, J. (1966), 'Pupil diameter and load on memory', *Science*, vol. 154, pp. 1583–5.

KAKOLEWSKI, J. W., and TAKEO, Y. (1967), 'Relationship between EEG patterns and arterial pressure changes', *Electroenceph. clin. Neurophysiol.*, vol. 22, pp. 239–44.

KIRK, R. E., and HECHT, E. (1963), 'Maintenance of vigilance by programmed noise', *Percept. mot. Skills*, vol. 16, pp. 553–60.

KLEINSMITH, L. J., and KAPLAN, S. (1963), 'Paired-associate learning as a function of arousal and interpolated learning', *J. exp. Psychol.*, vol. 65, pp. 190–93.

KLEITMAN, N. (1923), 'Studies in the physiology of sleep. IV. Further observations on the effects of prolonged sleeplessness', *Am. J. Psychol.*, vol. 109, p. 593.

KLEITMAN, N. (1939), *Sleep and Wakefulness*, University of Chicago Press.

KOEPKE, J. E., and PRIBRAM, K. H. (1966), 'Habituation of GSR as a function of stimulus duration and spontaneous activity', *J. comp physiol. Psychol.*, vol. 61, pp. 442–8.

KOGAN, A. B. (1960), 'The manifestations of processes of higher nervous activity in the electrical potentials of the cortex during free behavior of animals', in H. H. Jasper and G. D. Smirnow (eds.), *The Moscow Colloquium on Electroencephalography of Higher Nervous Activity*, *Electroenceph. clin. Neurophysiol.*, suppl. 13, pp. 51–64.

KOPELL, B. S., NOBLE, E. P., and SILVERMAN, J. (1965), 'The effect of thiamylal and methamphetamine on the two-flash fusion threshold', *Life Sciences*, vol. 2, pp. 2211–14.

KOOI, K. A., BAGCHI, B. K., and JORDAN, R. N. (1964), 'Observations on photically evoked occipital and vertex waves during sleep in man', in H. E. Whipple (ed), *Sensory Evoked Response in Man*, Annals N.Y. Acad. Sciences, vol. 112, pp. 270–80.

KORNETSKY, C., and BAIN, G. (1965), 'The effects of chlorpromazine and phenobarbitol on sustained attention in the rat', *Psychopharm.*, vol. 8, pp. 277–84.

KORNETSKY, C., MIRSKY, A. F., KESSLER, E. K., and DORFF, J. E. (1959), 'The effects of dextroamphetamine on behavioral deficits produced by sleep-loss in humans', *J. Pharmacol.*, vol. 127, pp. 46–50.

KREITMAN, N., and SHAW, J. C. (1965), 'Experimental enhancement of alpha activity', *Electroenceph. clin. Neurophysiol.*, vol. 18, pp. 147–55.

LACEY, J. I. (1950), 'Individual differences in somatic response patterns', *J. comp. physiol. Psychol.*, vol. 43, pp. 338–50.

LACEY, J. I. (1967), 'Somatic response patterning and stress: some revisions of activation theory', in M. H. Appley and R. Trumbull (eds.), *Psychological Stress*, Appleton-Century-Crofts, pp. 14–37.

LANSING, R. W., SCHWARTZ, E., and LINDSLEY, D. B. (1959), 'Reaction time and EEG activation under alerted and nonalerted conditions', *J. exp. Psychol.*, vol. 58, pp. 1–7.

LEAVY, A., and GREER, J. H. (1967), 'The effect of low levels of stimulus intensity upon the orienting response', *Psychon. Sci.*, vol. 9, pp. 105–6.

LEHMANN, D., BEELER, G. W., JR, and FENDER, D. H. (1965), 'Changes in patterns of the human electroencephalogram during fluctuation of perception of stabilized retinal images', *Electroenceph. clin. Neurophystol.*, vol. 19, pp. 336–43.

LEHMANN, D., BEELER, G. W., JR, and FENDER, D. H. (1967), 'EEG responses to light flashes during the observation of stabilized and normal retinal images', *Electroenceph. clin. Neurophysiol.*, vol. 22, pp. 136–42.

LESTER, B. K., and GUERRERO-FIGUEROA, R. (1966), 'Effects of some drugs on electroencephalographic fast activity and dream time', *Psychophysiol.*, vol. 2, pp. 224–36.

LEVINE, J. M. (1966), 'The effect of values and costs on the detection and identification of signals in auditory vigilance', *Human Factors*, vol. 8, pp. 525–38.

LEVONIAN, E. (1966), 'Evoked potential in relation to subsequent alpha frequency', *Science*, vol. 152, pp. 1280–82.

LIFSHITZ, K. (1966), 'The averaged evoked cortical response to complex visual stimuli', *Psychophysiol.*, vol. 3, pp. 55–68.

LINDSLEY, D. B. (1952), 'Psychological phenomena and the electro-encephalogram', *Electroenceph. clin. Neurophystol.*, vol. 4, pp. 443–56.

LINDSLEY, D. B. (1960), 'Attention, consciousness, sleep and wakefulness', in J. Field (ed.), *Handbook of Physiology*, Am. Physiol. Soc., sect. 1, vol. 3, pp. 1553–94.

LOEB, M., and BINFORD, J. R. (1968), 'Variation in performance on auditory and visual monitoring tasks as a function of signal and stimulus frequencies', *Perception and Psychophysics*, vol. 4, pp. 361–7.

LOEB, M., HAWKES, G. R., EVANS, W. O., and ALLUISI, E. A. (1965), 'The influence of d-amphetamine, benactyzine, and chlorpromazine on performance in an auditory vigilance task', *Psychon. Sci.*, vol. 3, pp. 29–30.

LOEB, M., and JEANTHEAU, G. (1958), 'The influence of noxious environmental stimulation on vigilance', *J. appl. Psychol.*, vol. 44, pp. 47–9.

LUCE, T. S. (1964), 'Vigilance as a function of stimulus variety and response complexity', *Human Factors*, vol. 6, pp. 101–10.

LYNN, R. (1966), *Attention, Arousal and the Orientation Reaction*, Pergamon Press.

MACADAR, O., GINES, A., BOVE, I. C., and GARCÍA-AUSTT, E. (1963), 'Effect of habituation, interference and association of stimuli upon the visual evoked response in the rat', *Act. neurol. Lat. Amer.*, vol. 9, pp. 315–27.

MACKWORTH, J. F. (1963a), 'The relation between the visual image and post-perceptual immediate memory', *J. verb. Learn. verb. Behav.*, vol. 2, pp. 75–85.

MACKWORTH, J. F. (1963b), 'Effect of reference marks on the detection of signals on a clock-face', *J. appl. Psychol.*, vol. 47, pp. 196–201.

MACKWORTH, J. F. (1964), 'Performance decrement in vigilance, threshold determinations and high-speed motor tasks', *Canad. J. Psychol.*, vol. 18, pp. 209–23.

MACKWORTH, J. F. (1965), 'The effect of amphetamine on the detectability of signals in a vigilance task', *Canad. J. Psychol.*, vol. 19, pp. 104–9.

MACKWORTH, J. F. (1966), 'Perceptual coding as a factor in short term memory', *Canad. J. Psychol.*, vol. 20, pp. 18–33.

MACKWORTH, J. F. (1968a), 'Vigilance, arousal and habituation', *Psychol. Rev.*, vol. 75, pp. 308–22.

MACKWORTH, J. F. (1968b), 'The effect of signal rate on performance in two kinds of vigilance task', *Human Factors*, vol. 10, pp. 11–18.

MACKWORTH, J. F. (1970), *Vigilance and Attention: A Signal Detection Approach*, Penguin Books.

MACKWORTH, J. F., and TAYLOR, M. M. (1963), 'The d' measure of signal detectability in vigilance-like situations', *Canad. J. Psychol.*, vol. 17, pp. 302–25.

MACKWORTH, N. H. (1950), *Researches in the Measurement of Human Performance*, M.R.C. Spec. Rpt 268, H.M.S.O. Reprinted in H. W. Sinaiko (ed.), *Selected Papers on Human Factors in the Design and Use of Control Systems*, Dover Publications, 1961, pp. 174–331.

MACKWORTH, N. H. (1957), 'Vigilance', *The Advancement of Science*, vol. 53, pp. 389–93.

MAGOUN, H. W. (1963), 'Central neural inhibition', in M. R. Jones (ed.), *Nebraska Symposium on Motivation*, University of Nebraska Press, pp. 191–3.

MAGOUN, H. W. (1965), *The Waking Brain*, Charles C. Thomas.

MALMO, R. B. (1959), 'Activation: a neuropsychological dimension', *Psychol. Rev.*, vol. 66, pp. 367–86.

MARSH, J. T., MCCARTHY, D. O., SHEATZ, G., and GALAMBOS, R. (1961), 'Amplitude changes in evoked auditory potentials during habituation and conditioning', *Electroenceph. clin. Neurophysiol.*, vol. 13, pp. 224–34.

MARSH, J. T., and WORDEN, F. G. (1964), 'Auditory potentials during acoustic habituation: cochlear nucleus, cerebellum and auditory cortex', *Electroenceph. clin. Neurophysiol.*, vol. 17, pp. 685–92.

MCBAIN, W. N. (1961), 'Noise, the "arousal hypothesis" and monotonous work', *J. appl. Psychol.*, vol. 45, pp. 309–17.

MCCORMACK, P. D. (1960), 'Performance in a vigilance task as a function of length of inter-stimulus interval', *Canad. J. Psychol.*, vol. 14, pp. 265–8.

MCDANIEL, J. W., and WHITE, R. K. (1966), 'A factorial study of the stimulus conditions of habituation', *Percept. mot. Skills*, vol. 23, pp. 259–70.

MCFARLAND, R. A., HOLWAY, A. N., and HURVISH, L. M. (1942), *Studies of Visual Fatigue*, Harvard Graduate School of Business Administration Rpt, p. 160.

MCGRATH, J. J. (1960), 'The effect of irrelevant environmental stimulation on vigilance performance', *Technical Rpt*, no. 6, Human Factors Research, Los Angeles.

MCGRATH, J. J. (1963a), 'Irrelevant stimulation and vigilance performance', in D. N. Buckner and J. J. McGrath (eds.), *Vigilance: A Symposium*, McGraw-Hill, pp. 3–18.

MCGRATH, J. J. (1963b), 'Cross-validation of some correlates of vigilance performance', in D. N. Buckner and J. J. McGrath (eds.), *Vigilance: A Symposium*, McGraw-Hill, pp. 118–23.

MCGRATH, J. J. (1963c), 'Some problems of definition and criteria in the study of vigilance performance', in D. N. Buckner and J. J. McGrath (eds.), *Vigilance: A Symposium*, McGraw-Hill, pp. 227–36.

MCGRATH, J. J. (1965), 'Performance sharing in an audio-visual task', *Human Factors*, vol. 7, pp. 141–54.

MCGRATH, J. J., and HARABEDIAN, A. (1963), 'Signal detection as a function of intersignal-interval duration', in D. N. Buckner and J. J. McGrath (eds.), *Vigilance: A Symposium*, McGraw-Hill, pp. 102–9.

MCGRATH, J. J., HARABEDIAN, A., and BUCKNER, D. N. (1959), 'Review and critique of the literature on vigilance performance',

Technical Rpt, no. 1, Human Factors Research, Los Angeles.

McNULTY, J. A., and NOSEWORTHY, W. J. (1966), 'Physiological response specificity, arousal and task performance', *Percept. mot. Skills*, vol. 23, pp. 987–96.

MICKO, H. C. (1966), 'Vigilance, arousal *v.* reinforcement', *Quart. J. exp. Psychol.*, vol. 18, pp. 39–46.

MIRABELLA, A., and GOLDSTEIN, D. A. (1967), 'The effects of ambient noise upon signal detection', *Human Factors*, vol. 9, pp. 277–84.

MIRSKY, A. F., and KORNETSKY, C. (1964), 'On the dissimilar effects of drugs on the digit symbol substitution and continuous performance tests', *Psychopharm.* (Berl.), vol. 5, pp. 161–77.

MONNIER, M., KALBERE, M., and KRUPP, P. (1960), 'Functional antagonism between diffuse reticular and intralaminary recruiting projections in the medial thalamus', *Exp. Neurol.*, vol. 2, pp. 271–89.

MORELL, L. K. (1965), 'EEG correlates of reaction time: a study of background and light-evoked potentials', *Electroenceph. clin. Neurophysiol.*, vol. 18, p. 523.

MORELL, L. K. (1966), 'Some characteristics of stimulus-provoked alpha activity', *Electroenceph. clin. Neurophysiol.*, vol. 21, pp. 552–61.

MORISON, R. S., and DEMPSEY, E. W. (1942), 'A study of thalamo-cortical relations', *Am. J. Physiol.*, vol. 135, pp. 281–92.

MORUZZI, G., and MAGOUN, H. W. (1949), 'Brain stem reticular formation and activation of the EEG', *Electroenceph. clin. Neurophysiol.*, vol. 1, pp. 455–73.

MUNDY-CASTLE, A. C., and McKIEVER, B. L. (1953), 'The psycho-physiological significance of the galvanic skin response', *J. exp. Psychol.*, vol. 46, pp. 15–24.

NADEL, L. (1966), 'Cortical spreading depression and habituation', *Psychon. Sci.*, vol. 5, pp. 119–20.

NEAL, G. L., and PEARSON, R. G. (1966), 'Comparative effects of age, sex and drugs upon two tasks of auditory vigilance', *Percept. mot. Skills*, vol. 23, pp. 967–74.

NEBYLITSYN, V. D. (1966), *Fundamental Properties of the Human Nervous System*, Akad. Padegog. Nauk., R.S.F.S.R., Moscow (Russian).

NIEMAYER, R. C., and SIEGEL, S. (1967), 'Effects of phenobarbital sodium on spontaneous motor activity', *Psychon. Sci.*, vol. 9, pp. 47–8.

NISHISATO, S. (1966), 'Reaction time as a function of arousal and anxiety', *Psychon. Sci.*, pp. 157–8.

O'HANLON, J. (1964), 'Adrenalin, noradrenalin and performance in a visual vigilance task', Rpt no. 750–5, Human Factors Research, Los Angeles. Reprinted in *Science*, vol. 150 (1965), pp. 507–9.

O'HANLON, J., SCHMIDT, A., and BAKER, C. H. (1965), 'Doppler discrimination and the effect of a visual alertness indication upon detection of auditory sonar signals in a sonar watch', *Human Factors*, vol. 12, no. 7, pp. 129–40.

OLDFIELD, R. C. (1937), 'Some recent experiments bearing upon internal inhibition', *Brit. J. Psychol.*, vol. 28, p. 28.

ORNITZ, E. M., RITVO, E. R., CARR, E. M., LA FRANCHI, S., and WALTER, R. D. (1967), 'The effect of sleep onset on the auditory averaged evoked response', *Electroencephal. clin. Neurophysiol.*, vol. 23, pp. 335–41.

OSTFELD, A. M., MACHNE, X., and UNNA, K. R. (1960), 'The effects of atropine on the electroencephalogram and behavior in man', *J. Pharm. exp. Therapeutics*, vol. 128, pp. 265–72.

OSWALD, I. (1962), *Sleeping and Waking*, Elsevier.

PATRICK, G. T. W., and GILBERT, J. A. (1896), 'On the effects of loss of sleep', *Psychol. Rev.*, vol. 3, pp. 469–83.

PAVLOV, I. (1927), *Conditioned Reflexes*, Oxford University Press.

PAYNE, R. B., and HAUTY, G. T. (1954), 'The effects of experimentally induced attitudes upon task proficiency', *J. exp. Psychol.*, vol. 47, pp. 267–73.

PAYNE, R. B., and HAUTY, G. T. (1955), 'Effects of psychological feedback upon work decrement', *J. exp. Psychol.*, vol. 50, pp. 343–51.

PAYNE, R. B., HAUTY, G. T., and MOORE, E. W. (1957), 'Restoration of tracking proficiency as a function of amount and delay of analeptic medication', *J. comp. physiol. Psychol.*, vol. 50, pp. 146–9.

PEPLER, R. D. (1958), 'Warmth and performance: an investigation in the tropics', *Ergonomics*, vol. 2, pp. 63–88.

PEPLER, R. D. (1959), 'Warmth and lack of sleep: accuracy or activity reduced', *J. comp. physiol. Psychol.*, vol. 52, pp. 446–50.

PEPLER, R. D. (1960), 'Warmth, glare and a background of quiet speech: a comparison of their effects on performance', *Ergonomics*, vol. 3, pp. 68–73.

PERRY, N. W., and COPENHAVER, R. M. (1965), 'Differential cortical habituation with stimulation of central and peripheral retina', *Percept. mot. Skills*, vol. 20, pp. 1209–13.

PICKENS, R., MEISCH, R., and MCGUIRE, L. E. (1967), 'Methamphetamine reinforcement in rats', *Psychon. Sci.*, vol. 8, pp. 371–2.

PODVOLL, E. M., and GOODMAN, S. J. (1967), 'Averaged neural electrical activity and arousal', *Science*, vol. 155, pp. 223–5.

POLIDORA, V. J., and URBANEK, R. J. (1964), 'Drug effects upon visual signal-from-noise detection by monkeys', *Psychon. Sci.*, vol. 1, pp. 237–38.

POULTON, E. C. (1960), 'The optimal perceptual load in a paced auditory inspection task', *Brit. J. Psychol.*, vol. 51, pp. 127–39.

POULTON, E. C. (1966), 'Engineering psychology', *Ann. Rev. Psychol.* vol. 17, pp. 177–200.

POULTON, E. C., HITCHINGS, N. B., and BROOKE, R. B. (1965),

'Effect of cold and rain upon the vigilance of lookouts', *Ergonomics*, vol. 8, pp. 163–8.

POULTON, E. C., and KERSLAKE, D. M. (1965), 'The initial stimulating effect of warmth upon perceptual efficiency', *Aerospace Medicine*, vol. 36, pp. 29–32.

PRIBRAM, K. H. (1967), 'The limbic systems, efferent control of neural inhibition and behavior', *Progress in Brain Research*, Elsevier vol. 27, pp. 318–36,

RAPIN, I. (1964), 'Evoked responses to clicks in a group of children with communication disorders', in H. E. Whipple (ed.), *Sensory Evoked Response in Man*, Annals N.Y. Acad. Sciences, pp. 182–203.

REBERT, C. S., McADAM, D. W., KNOTT, J. R., and IRWIN, D. A. (1967), 'Slow potential change in human brain related to level of motivation', *J. comp. physiol. Psychol.*, vol. 36, pp. 20–23.

RODIN, E. A., GRISELL, J. L., GUDOBBA, R. D., and ZACHARY, G. (1965), 'Relationship of EEG background, rhythms to photic evoked responses', *Electroenceph. clin. Neurophysiol.*, vol. 19, pp. 301–4.

ROSE, G. H., and LINDSLEY, D. B. (1965), 'Visually evoked electro-cortical responses in kittens: development of specific and nonspecific systems', *Science*, vol. 148, pp. 1244–6.

ROSENQUIST, H. S. (1965), 'The visual response component of rotary pursuit tracking', *Percept. mot. Skills*, vol. 21, pp. 555–60.

ROSS, S., DARDANO, J. F., and HACKMAN, R. C. (1959), 'Conductance levels during vigilance task performance', *J. appl. Psychol.*, vol. 43, pp. 65–9.

ROZHDESTVENSKAYA, V. I., and YERMOLAYEVA-TOMINA, L. L. B. (1966), 'A study of mental capacity for work in relation to typological characteristics of the nervous system', *Proc. 18th Int. Cong. exp. Psychol., Moscow, Ninth Symposium*, pp. 51–9.

RYLE, G. (1948), *The Concept of Mind*, Barnes and Noble.

SALDANHA, E. L. (1955), 'An investigation into the effects of prolonged and exacting visual work', A.P.U. 243, Applied Psychology Research Unit, Cambridge.

SANDERS, A. G. (ed.) (1967), *Attention and Performance*, Reprinted in *Acta Psychologica*, vol. 27.

SCOTT, T. H. (1957), *Literature Review of the Intellectual Effects of Perceptual Isolation*, Defence Research Board, Canada, Rpt HR. 66.

SCOTT, W. E. (1966), 'Activation theory and task design', *Organ. Behav. hum. Perf.*, vol. 1, pp. 3–30.

SEASHORE, R. H., and IVY, A. C. (1953), 'Effects of analeptic drugs in relieving fatigue', *Psychol. Monog.*, vol. 67, no. 15, pp. 1–16.

SHARPLESS, S., and JASPER, H. H. (1956), 'Habituation of the arousal reaction', *Brain*, vol. 79, pp. 655–80.

SHAW, J. A., and THOMPSON, R. F. (1964a), 'Dependence of evoked cortical association responses on behavioral variables', *Psychon. Sci.*, vol. 1, pp. 153–4.

SHAW, J. A., and THOMPSON, R. F. (1964b), 'Inverse relation between evoked cortical association responses and behavioral orienting to repeated auditory stimuli', *Psychon. Sci.*, vol. 1, pp. 399–400.

SHERWOOD, J. J. (1965), 'A relation between arousal and performance', *Am. J. Psychol.*, vol. 78, pp. 461–5.

SIDALL, G. J., and ANDERSON, D. M. (1955), 'Fatigue during prolonged performance on a simple compensatory tracking task', *Quart. J. exp. Psychol.*, vol. 7, pp. 159–65.

SINGLETON, W. T. (1953), 'Deterioration of performance on a short-term perceptual-motor task', in W. F. Floyd and A. T. Welford (eds.), *Symposium on Fatigue*, H. K. Lewis, pp. 163–72.

SIPOWICZ, R. R., and BAKER, R. A. (1961), 'Effects of intelligence on vigilance: a replication', *Percept. mot. Skills*, vol. 13, p. 398.

SKINNER, B. F. (1938), *The Behavior of Organisms*, Appleton-Century-Crofts.

SMITH, C. B. (1964), 'Effects of d-amphetamine upon operant behavior of pigeons: enhancement by reserpine', *J. Pharm. exp. Therapeutics*, vol. 146, pp. 167–74.

SMITH, S., MYERS, T. I., and MURPHY, D. B., (1967), 'Vigilance during sensory deprivation', *Percept. mot. Skills*, vol. 24, pp. 971–6.

SOKOLOV, E. N. (1963), *Perception and the Conditioned Reflex*, Pergamon Press and Macmillan.

SOLANDT, D. Y., and PARTRIDGE, R. C. (1946), 'Research on auditory problems presented by naval operations', *J. Canad. med. Services*, vol. 3, pp. 323–9.

SPONG, P., HAIDER, M., and LINDSLEY, D. B. (1965), 'Selective attentiveness and evoked cortical responses to visual and auditory stimuli', *Science*, vol. 148, pp. 395–7.

STELLAR, E. (1960), 'Drive and motivation', in J. Field (ed.), *Handbook of Physiology*, American Physiological Society, sect. 1, vol. 3, pp. 1501–28.

STENNETT, R. G. (1957), 'The relationship of performance level to level of arousal', *J. exp. Psychol.*, vol. 54, pp. 54–61.

STERN, R. M. (1964), 'Electrophysiological effects of the interaction between task demands and sensory input', *Canad. J. Psychol.*, vol. 18, pp. 311–20.

STERN, R. M. (1966), 'Performance and physiological arousal during two vigilance tasks varying in signal presentation rate', *Percept. mot. Skills*, vol. 23, pp. 691–700.

SURWILLO, W. W. (1963), 'The relation of simple response time to brain wave frequency and the effects of age', *Electroenceph. clin. Neurophysiol.*, vol. 15, pp. 105–14.

SURWILLO, W. W. (1967a), 'Relation of latency of galvanic skin reflex to frequency of the electroencephalogram', *Psychon. Sci.*, vol. 7, pp. 303–4.

SURWILLO, W. W. (1967b), 'The influence of some psychological factors on latency of the galvanic skin reflex', *Psychophysiol.*, vol. 4, pp. 223–8.

SURWILLO, W. W., and QUILTER, R. E. (1965), 'The relation of frequency of spontaneous skin potential responses to vigilance and to age', *Psychophysiol.*, vol. 1, pp. 272–6.

SUTTON, S., BRAREN, M., JOHN, E. R., and ZUBIN, J. (1965), 'Evoked potential correlates of stimulus uncertainty', *Science*, vol. 150, p. 1187.

TALLAND, G. A., and QUARTON, G. C. (1966), 'The effects of drugs and familiarity on performance in continuous visual search', *J. nerv. ment. Dis.*, vol. 143, pp. 266–74.

TARRIÈRE, C., and HARTEMANN, F. (1964), 'Investigation into the effects of tobacco smoke on a visual vigilance task', *Ergonomics*, Proceedings of 2nd I.E.A. Congress, Dortmund, pp. 525–30.

TARRIÈRE, C., and WISNER, A. (1962), 'Effets des bruits significatifs et non-significatifs au cours d'une épreuve de vigilance', *Le Travail Humain*, vol. 1–2, pp. 1–28.

TAYLOR, M. M. (1966), 'The effect of the square root of time on continuing perceptual tasks', *Percept. Psychophysics*, vol. 1, pp. 113–19.

TEICHNER, W. H. (1962), 'Probability of detection and speed of response in simple monitoring', *Human Factors*, vol. 4, pp. 181–6.

TEICHNER, W. H., and KOBRICK, J. L. (1955,) 'Effects of prolonged exposure to low temperature on visual motor performance', *J. exp. Psychol.*, vol. 49, pp. 122–6.

TEICHNER, W. H., and WEHRKAMP, R. F. (1954), 'Visual-motor performance as a function of short duration ambient temperature', *J. exp. Psychol.*, vol. 47, pp. 447–50.

TEPLOV, B. M. (1964), 'Problems in the study of general types of higher nervous activity in man and animals', in J. A. Gray (ed.), *Pavlov's Typology*, Pergamon Press, pp. 3–153.

THOMPSON, R. F. (1967), *Foundations of Physiological Psychology*, Harper and Row.

THOMPSON, R. F., DENNY, D., and SMITH, H. E. (1966), 'Cortical control of specific and nonspecific sensory projections to the cerebral cortex', *Psychon. Sci.*, vol. 4, pp. 93–4.

THOMPSON, R. F., and SHAW, J. A. (1965), 'Behavioral correlates of evoked activity recorded from association areas of the cerebral cortex', *J. comp. physiol. Psychol.*, vol. 60, pp. 329–39.

THOMPSON, R. F., and SPENCER, W. A. (1966), 'Habituation: a model phenomenon for the study of neuronal substrates of behavior', *Psychol. Rev.*, vol. 173, pp. 16–43.

THOMPSON, R. F., and WALKER, W. I. (1963), 'Role of auditory cortex in reflex head orientation in cats to auditory stimuli', *J. comp. physiol. Psychol,*, vol. 56, pp. 996–1002.

THORSHEIM, H. I. (1967), 'EEG and vigilance behavior', *Psychon. Sci.*, vol. 8, pp. 499–500.

TISSOT, R., and BOVET, J. (1967), 'Modifications de l'habituation de la réaction d'arrêt du rhythme chez l'homme sous l'effet de la chlorpromazine et du haloperidol', *Psychopharm.* (Berl.), vol. 10, pp. 298–307.

TYLER, D. B. (1947), 'The effect of amphetamine sulphate and some barbiturates on the fatigue produced by prolonged wakefulness', *Am. J. Physiol.*, vol. 149, pp. 185–93.

TYLER, D. B., GOODMAN, J., and ROTHMAN, T. (1947), 'The effect of experimental insomnia on the rate of potential changes in the brain', *Am. J. Physiol.*, vol. 149, pp. 185–93.

UEHLING, B. S., and VENATOR, E. R. (1967), 'Effects of d-amphetamine and phenobarbitol on vigilance in the rat', *Psychon. Sci.*, vol. 9, pp. 113–14.

URSIN, H., WESTER, K., and URSIN, R. (1967), 'Habituation to electrical stimulation of the brain in unanesthetized cats', *Electroenceph. clin. Neurophysiol.*, vol. 23, pp. 41–9.

VENABLES, P. H. (1963), 'The measurement of level of arousal', *J. psychiatric Res.*, vol. 1, p. 279.

WALLIS, D., and SAMUEL, J. A. (1961), 'Some experimental studies of radar operating', *Ergonomics*, vol. 4, pp. 155–68.

WALTER, W. G. (1964a), 'The convergence and interaction of visual, auditory and tactile responses in human non-specific cortex', in H. E. Whipple (ed.), *Sensory Evoked Response in Man*, Annals N.Y. Acad. Sciences, vol. 112, pp. 320–61.

WALTER, W. G. (1964b), 'Slow potential waves in the human brain associated with expectancy, attention and decision', *Arch. Psych. Zeitschrift f.d. ges. Neurologie*, vol. 206, pp. 309–22.

WALTER, W. G., COOPER, R., ALDRIDGE, V. J., McCALLUM, W. C., and WINTER, A. L. (1964), 'Contingent negative variation: an electric sign of sensory motor association and expectancy in the human brain', *Nature*, vol. 203, pp. 380–84.

WARE, J. R. (1961), 'Effects of intelligence on signal detection in visual and auditory monitoring', *Percept. mot. Skills*, vol. 13, pp. 99–102.

WARE, J. R., BAKER, R. A., and DRUCKER, E. (1964), 'Sustained vigilance: II. Signal detection for two-man teams during a 24-hour watch', *J. engin. Psychol.*, vol. 3, pp. 104–10.

WARE, J. R., BAKER, R. A., and SIPOWICZ, R. R. (1962),' Performance of mental deficients in a simple vigilance task', *Am. J. ment. Deficiency*, vol. 66, pp. 647–50.

WARREN, N., and CLARKE, B., (1937), 'Blocking in mental and motor tasks during a 65-hour vigil', *J. exp. Psychol.*, vol. 21, pp. 97–105.

WARWICK, K. M., and EYSENCK, H. J. (1963), 'The effects of smoking on the CFF threshold', *Life Sciences*, vol. 4, pp. 219–25.

WATKINS, W. H. (1966), 'Photic facilitation of tonal signal detection in a forced situation', *Psychon. Sci.*, vol. 6, pp. 477–8.

WEBSTER, W. R., DUNLOP, C. W., SIMONS, L. A., and AITKEN,

L. M. (1965), 'Auditory habituation: a test of a centrifugal and peripheral theory', *Science*, vol. 148, pp. 654–6.

WEINER, H., and ROSS, S. (1962), 'The effects of "unwanted" signals and d-amphetamine sulphate on observer responses', *J. appl. Psychol.*, vol. 46, pp. 135–41.

WEISS, B., and LATIES, V. G. (1962), 'Enhancement of human performance by caffeine and the amphetamines', *Pharmacol. Reviews*, vol. 14, pp. 1–36.

WEITZMAN, E. D., and KREMEN, H. (1965), 'Auditory evoked responses during different stages of sleep in man', *Electroenceph. clin. Neurophysiol.*, vol. 18, pp. 65–70.

WELFORD, A. T., and BIRREN, J. E. (1965), *Behavior, Aging and the Nervous System*, Thomas.

WENGER, M. A. (1941), 'The measurement of individual differences in autonomic balance', *Psychosom. Medicine*, vol. 3, pp. 427–34.

WHIPPLE, H. E. (ed.) (1964), *Sensory Evoked Response in Man*, Annals N.Y. Acad. Sciences, vol. 112.

WHITE, C. T., and EASON, R. G. (1966), 'Evoked cortical potentials in relation to certain aspects of visual perception', *Psychol. Monogr.*, vol. 80, no. 24, whole no. 632.

WICKE, L. D., DONCHIN, E., and LINDSLEY, D. B. (1964), 'Visual evoked potentials as a function of flash luminance and duration', *Science*, vol. 148, pp. 395–7.

WIENER, E. L., POOCK, G. K., and STEELE, M. (1964), 'Effect of time-sharing on monitoring performance: simple arithmetic as a loading task', *Percept. mot. Skills*, vol. 19, pp. 435–40.

WILDER, J. (1957), 'The law of initial value in neurology and psychiatry: facts and problems', *J. nerv. ment. Dis.*, vol. 125, pp. 73–86.

WILKINSON, R. T. (1959), 'Rest pauses in a task affected by lack of sleep', *Ergonomics*, vol. 2, pp. 373–80.

WILKINSON, R. T. (1960), 'The effect of lack of sleep on visual watchkeeping', *Quart. J. exp. Psychol.*, vol. 7, pp. 36–40.

WILKINSON, R. T. (1961), 'Interaction of lack of sleep with knowledge of results, repeated testing and individual differences', *J. exp. Psychol.*, vol. 62, pp. 263–71.

WILKINSON, R. T. (1962), 'Muscle tension during mental work under sleep deprivation', *J. exp. Psychol.*, vol. 64, pp. 565–71.

WILKINSON, R. T. (1963a), 'After-effect of sleep deprivation', *J. exp. Psychol.*, vol. 66, pp. 439–42.

WILKINSON, R. T. (1963b), 'Interaction of noise with knowledge of results and sleep deprivation', *J. exp. Psychol.*, vol. 66, pp. 332–7.

WILKINSON, R. T. (1964), 'Effects of up to 60 hours' sleep deprivation on different types of work', *Ergonomics*, vol. 7, pp. 175–86.

WILKINSON, R. T. (1968), 'Sleep deprivation: performance tests for partial and selective sleep deprivation', in L. A. Abt and B. F. Riess (eds.), *Progress in Clinical Psychology*, Grune and Stratton, vol. 7.

WILKINSON, R. T., EDWARDS, R. S., and HAINES, E. (1966), 'Performance following a night of reduced sleep', *Psychon. Sci.*, vol.5, pp. 471–2.

WILKINSON, R. T., FOX, R. H., GOLDSMITH, R., HAMPTON, I. F. G., and LEWIS, H. E. (1964), 'Psychological and physiological responses to raised body temperatures', *J. appl. Physiol.*, vol. 19, pp. 287–91.

WILKINSON, R. T., and MORLOCK, H. C. (1967), 'Auditory evoked response and reaction time', *Electroenceph. clin. Neurophysiol.*, vol. 23, pp. 50–56.

WILKINSON, R. T., MORLOCK, H. C., and WILLIAMS, H. L. (1966), 'Evoked cortical response during vigilance', *Psychon. Sci.*, vol. 4, pp. 221–2.

WILLIAMS, H. L. (1964), 'Decrement in performance due to sleep deprivation', *Symposium on Medical Aspects of Stress in the Military Climate*, Walter Reed Army Institute of Research, Washington, pp. 187–202.

WILLIAMS, H. L., LUBIN, A., and GOODNOW, J. J. (1959), 'Impaired performance with acute sleep loss', *Psychol. Monogr.*, vol. 73, no. 484.

WILLIAMS, H. L., MORLOCK, H. C., MORLOCK, J. V., and LUBIN, A. (1964), 'Auditory evoked responses and the EEG stages of sleep', in H. E. Whipple (ed.), *Sensory Evoked Response in Man*, Annals N.Y. Acad. Sciences

WILLIAMS, H. L., TEPAS, D. I., and MORLOCK, H. C., (1962) 'Evoked response to clicks and electroencephalographic stages of sleep in man', *Science*, vol. 138, pp. 685–6.

WILLIAMS, J. A. (1963), 'Novelty, GSR and stimulus generalization', *Canad. J. Psychol.*, vol. 17, pp. 52–61.

WILSON, G. T., and RADLOFF, W. P. (1967), 'Degree of arousal and performance: effects of reticular stimulation on an operant task', *Psychon. Sci.*, vol. 7, pp. 13–14.

WILSON, J. C. (1965), 'An investigation of vigilance in the Rhesus monkey', *Quart. J. exp. Psychol.*, vol. 17, pp. 110–17.

WITKIN, H. A., DYKE, R. B., FATERSON, H. F., GOODENOUGH, D. R., and KARP, S. A. (1962), *Psychological Differentiation*, Wiley.

WOODHEAD, M. M. (1964a), 'Searching a visual display in intermittent noise', *J. Sound and Vibration*, vol. 1, pp. 157–61.

WOODHEAD, M. M. (1964b), 'The effects of bursts of noise on an arithmetic task', *Am. J. Psychol.*, vol. 77, pp. 627–33.

WOODWORTH, R. S., and SCHLOSBERG, H. (1954), *Experimental Psychology*, Henry Holt.

WORDEN, F. G., and MARSH, J. T. (1963), 'Amplitude changes of auditory potentials evoked at cochlear nucleus during acoustic habituation', *Electroenceph. clin. Neurophysiol.*, vol. 16, pp. 866–81.

ZUBEK, J. P. (1964), 'Effects of prolonged sensory and perceptual deprivation', *Brit. med. Bull.*, vol. 20, pp. 38–42.

ZUBEK, J. P. and MACNEILL, M. (1966), 'Effects of immobilization:

behavioral and EEG changes', *Canad. J. Psychol.* vol. 20, pp. 316–36.

ZUBEK, J. P., PUSHKAR, D., SANSOM, W., and GOWING, J. (1961), 'Perceptual changes after prolonged sensory isolation (darkness and silence)', *Canad. J. Psychol.*, vol. 15, pp. 83–100.

ZUERCHER, J. D. (1965), 'The effects of extraneous stimulation on vigilance', *Human Factors*, vol. 7, pp. 101–6.

ZWISLOCKI, J., MAIRE, F., FELDMAN, A. S., and RUBIN, H. (1958), 'On the effect of practice and motivation on the threshold of audibility', *J. acoust. Soc. Am.*, vol. 30, pp. 254–62.

Acknowledgements

Thanks are due to the authors of each figure for their permission to reproduce. Full reference will be found in the bibliography. Thanks are also due to the following publishers for permission to reproduce copyright material:

Figures 24, 25   Academic Press
Figures 12, 16   *Acta Neurologica Latin America*
Figure 30   American Physiological Association
Figures 13, 19, 20, 21, 22, 29, 31   American Psychological Association
Figure 18   *Brain*
Figure 4   British Psychological Society
Figures 2, 3, 27   Canadian Psychological Society
Figures 9, 11, 15   Elsevier Publishing Co.
Figures 1, 28   Her Majesty's Stationery Office
Figure 10   *Perceptual and Motor Skills*
Figure 26   Presses Universitaires de France
Figure 23   *Psychological Record*
Figures 17, 32   Psychonomic Journals Inc.
Figures 6, 7, 8, 14   *Science* and the American Association for the Advancement of Science
Figures 33, 34   Taylor and Francis Ltd

Index